Math Logic & Word Problems

5-6

Written by
Angela Higgs

Editors: Carla Hamaguchi and Collene Dobelmann
Illustrator: Corbin Hillam
Designer/Production: Moonhee Pak/Cari Helstrom
Cover Designer: Barbara Peterson
Art Director: Tom Cochrane
Project Director: Carolea Williams

Reprinted 2012

Table of Contents

Introduction

Each book in the *Power Practice*™ series contains over 100 ready-to-use activity pages to provide students with skill practice. The fun activities can be used to supplement and enhance what you are already teaching in your classroom. Give an activity page to students as independent class work, or send the pages home as homework to reinforce skills taught in class. An answer key is provided for quick reference.

Math Logic & Word Problems 5–6 provides activities that will directly assist students in practicing and solving logic and problem-solving challenges, as well as reinforcing math skills such as decimals, fractions, addition, subtraction, multiplication, division, graphing, time, probability, and more! The book is organized by the National Council of Teachers of Mathematics (NCTM) standards and contains motivating activities that cover number and operations, algebra, geometry, measurement, and data analysis and probability.

The activities include various types of logic questions. The activities are grouped in "sets" that cover each type of question. The first activity page of each set includes a brief explanation of which strategies to use to complete the problem. These pages include a section called "Strategic Steps" that explain how to solve the problem. The subhead *Show Me the Way* identifies these types of pages. The remaining pages offer students a chance to independently practice using the strategies and steps to solve similar problems.

Use these ready-to-go activities to "recharge" skill review and give students the power to succeed!

Place Value

SHOW ME THE WAY

Ashley needs help to correct her math homework. She is having trouble with lining up problems to add and everything is in the wrong place. Can you help her?

A. 245.6
98.00
123.4
2.456

Hundred thousands	Ten thousands	Thousands	Hundreds	Tens	Ones	Decimal	Tenths	Hundredths	Thousandths
						•			
						•			
						•			
						•			
						•			

Total

Strategic Steps

1 Remember that you need to line up the decimal points so that the similar place values are aligned. The problem Ashley has is that her numbers are lined up haphazardly instead of by place value.

2 The first number has a 2 in the hundreds place, a 4 in the tens place, a 5 in the ones place, and a decimal followed by the 6 in the tenths place. Write this number on the chart by placing each number in the correct place-value position.

3 The second number has a 9 in the tens place. Place this number in the correct position on the chart.

4 Repeat for the other two numbers.

5 Now that the numbers are lined up correctly, add the numbers together.

Math Logic & Word Problems • 5–6 © 2005 Creative Teaching Press

What Place?

Bryan is having trouble lining up problems to add. Everything is in the wrong place. Help him solve the problems.

A. 42.104
543.72
50.837
+ 5216.8

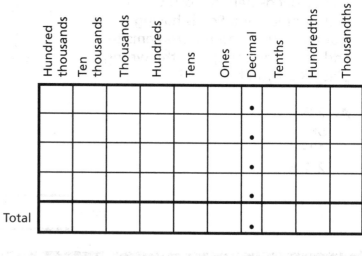

B. 4.215
38.07
240.7
+ 73.86

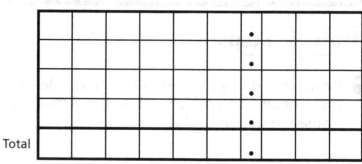

C. 42.104
4989.6
543.72
+ 3679.8

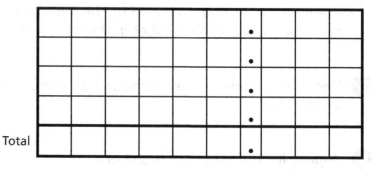

D. 738.9
528.65
3.765
+ 244

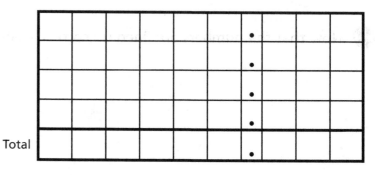

Math Logic & Word Problems • 5–6 © 2005 Creative Teaching Press

Name _____ Date _____

Number Arrangement

Align each number, then add.

	Hundred thousands	Ten thousands	Thousands	Hundreds	Tens	Ones	Decimal	Tenths	Hundredths	Thousandths

A. 523.165
      52.168
    242.41
 + 10.731

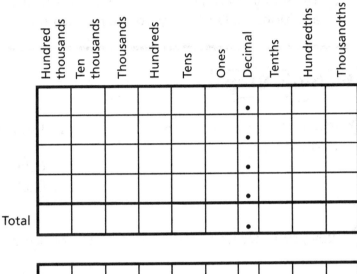

B. 54.3
    783.653
   2340.311
 + 14.307

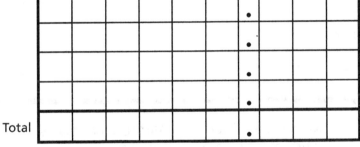

C. 483.44
    86.736
  1242.369
+ 896.896

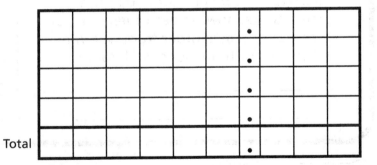

D. 5428.235
     1.458
   53.093
 + 158.09

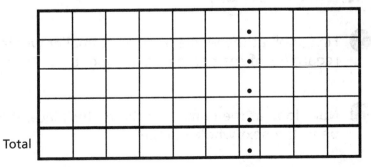

Decimals

Show Me the Way

A. Yesterday Sheri mowed 0.34 of the backyard. This morning she mowed an additional 0.43 of the yard. How much more does she have to mow?

Strategic Steps

1 The first step is to add the two decimals. Using vertical addition, line up the decimals and then add:

$$
\begin{array}{r}
0.34 \\
+\ 0.43 \\
\hline
\end{array}
$$

2 Now, subtract from 1, to represent the entire yard.

$$
\begin{array}{r}
1.00 \\
-\ \underline{}
\end{array}
$$
(answer from step 1)

B. Kathy, Lara, Madison, Aaron, and Wesley were practicing for a track meet. They each ran during practice today. Use the chart to see how far each friend ran, and then put them in order from who ran the shortest to the longest distance.

_____

_____

Name	Distance Ran
Kathy	3.7 miles
Lara	1.9 miles
Madison	0.45 miles
Aaron	2.01 miles
Wesley	0.64 miles

Strategic Steps

1 First, look at the whole number. A smaller whole number will have lesser value, regardless of the decimals following it.

2 Now, look at the number in the tenths place, the larger the number, the closer it will be to the next whole number.

Math Logic & Word Problems • 5–6 © 2005 Creative Teaching Press

More Decimals

A. For Pat's birthday he invited 2 friends over to watch movies. They ordered pizza and ate 0.33 of it. After the movie, the friends were talking and ate another 0.25 of the pizza. How much will be left for Pat's family to have for lunch the next day?

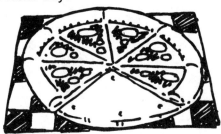

B. The school secretary was making copies of flyers to send home with all the students in the school. She used 1.33 packs of paper in the morning. She then used another 3.4 packs of paper in the afternoon. If she had 7 packs of paper when she began, how many are left?

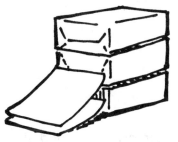

C. Nick was cleaning up after the PTA meeting. He collected all the opened and unopened juice bottles. There were 1.2 bottles of apple juice, 2 bottles of grape juice, 1.7 bottles of cranberry juice, and 0.3 bottle of fruit punch. How much drink was left after the meeting?

D. Kara's family is looking for a lot to build a new house. They looked at 5 lots and are trying to find the largest one. The lots are 1.74 acres, 1.705 acres, 1.07 acres, 1.75 acres, and 1.3 acres. Put the lots in order from smallest to largest.

Cameron's Day

A. For breakfast, Cameron drank 0.45 cup of water and 0.84 cup of orange juice. If he needs to drink 2 cups of fluid for breakfast, how much more does he need to drink?

B. On the bus ride home from school, Cameron read 0.25 of his history chapter. That afternoon he read another 0.33 of the chapter. While waiting for dinner he read another 0.145 of the chapter. How much does he have left to read after dinner?

C. Cameron weighed all the animals in his toy animal collection. The table below shows the weights. Put them in order from greatest to least weight.

Animal	Weight
Fox	.75 g
Beaver	1.2 g
Deer	1.34 g
Alligator	.83 g
Buffalo	.98 g

D. Cameron and his dad have been working on building a model train layout. The first month they put down 3.2 feet of track. The second month they removed 1.15 feet of track and then put down 1.4 feet of track. The third month they removed 2 feet of track and then finished the tracks by adding an additional 5.7 feet of track. How long was the completed track?

Math Logic & Word Problems • 5–6 © 2005 Creative Teaching Press

Peanut Hunt

Show Me the Way

Mrs. Brozack hid 100 peanuts in the schoolyard and challenged her students to find them all. They hunted in the playground and found 23 peanuts. Then they went to the front of the school and checked under the shrubs and around the trees and found another 15. Then they searched the shrubbery in front of the teacher's parking lot and found another 24 peanuts. The area around the soccer field yielded another 34 peanuts. The students said, "Mrs. Brozack, we found all the peanuts, we searched everywhere!"

Mrs. Brozack replied, "Are you certain you found *all* the peanuts?"

How do you know how many peanuts were found? Did the students find all 100 hidden peanuts?

Strategic Steps

1 The problem states that 100 peanuts were hidden. The students found peanuts in 4 areas. To find out how many they found, add the numbers.

$$23 + 15 + 24 + 34 = \text{_____} \text{ total number of peanuts found}$$

2 Compare the total number of peanuts found to 100, is it the same? If not, then the students did not find all the peanuts.

Math Logic & Word Problems • 5–6 © 2005 Creative Teaching Press

Name _____ Date _____

Can Drive

Middletown School was collecting aluminum cans to raise money for new playground equipment. The sixth-grade class wanted to collect 785 cans to make enough money to pay for a bench for the teachers to sit next to the playground.

- The first week all the students collected cans in their neighborhoods and put up collection cans at the park. They collected 347 cans.

- The second week, they saved cans at home and then picked up the cans from the park. They collected another 179 cans.

- The third week was rainy and they were not able to collect the cans from the park. They only collected 63 cans.

- The fourth week there was nicer weather and they were able to collect the cans from the park. They collected a total of 204 cans.

Did they collect enough cans to buy the bench? Show your work.

Math Logic & Word Problems • 5–6 © 2005 Creative Teaching Press

Gold Rush

"Good Morning class," said Mr. Vincent. "Today we are going to go on a gold hunt. Our goal will be to mine for 50 pounds of gold nuggets."

"Well, actually not real gold. I've painted exactly 50 pounds of rocks with gold paint. They are all mixed with that huge pile of dirt that was dumped in the schoolyard."

The students' assignment was to use gold pans and a tub of water. They learned to swirl the pan to find the "gold" nuggets. It turned out to be a project that took several days. Each day they panned for gold and collected all the nuggets in a basin and then weighed them at the end of the day.

- Day one: They found 15 pounds, 6 ounces of "gold".

- Day two: They found 12 pounds, 8 ounces.

- Day three: They found 13 pounds, 14 ounces.

- Day four: They found 7 pounds, 2 ounces.

At the end of the fourth day, they only had a small amount of soil to pan. Do they need to continue, or have they found all 50 pounds of gold?

Math Logic & Word Problems • 5–6 © 2005 Creative Teaching Press

The Wedding

SHOW ME THE WAY

A. Jeanne was helping her sister Sam and her fiancée, Jack, plan their wedding. They have 187 guests attending.

Jeanne is trying to find how many tables will need to be set up in the reception hall. Each table will hold eight people. How many tables will they need?

Strategic Steps

1 To solve this problem, you need to divide the number of people attending the wedding by the number of people who can sit at a table.

$$187 \div 8 = \underline{\hspace{2cm}}$$

2 Remember, if 8 does not go into 187 evenly, the remainder, even if it is one person, will need a table to sit at.

B. Jeanne wants to put baskets with small bottles of bubbles around the room. The baskets will each hold 20 bottles. She wants to buy two bottles of bubbles for each guest. How many baskets will she need?

Strategic Steps

1 First, you need to find how many bottles of bubbles to buy. The problem says Jeanne wants to buy two bottles for each guest. There are 187 guests.

$$187 \times 2 = \underline{\hspace{2cm}}$$

2 Then, determine how many baskets you will need.

$$\underline{\hspace{2cm}} \div 20 = \underline{\hspace{2cm}}$$

Math Logic & Word Problems • 5–6 © 2005 Creative Teaching Press

Name _____ Date _____

National Parks

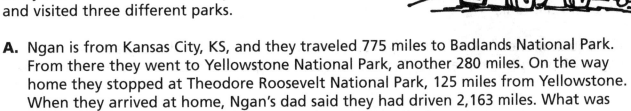

Ngan's family likes to visit national parks on vacation every summer. This summer they took off several weeks and visited three different parks.

A. Ngan is from Kansas City, KS, and they traveled 775 miles to Badlands National Park. From there they went to Yellowstone National Park, another 280 miles. On the way home they stopped at Theodore Roosevelt National Park, 125 miles from Yellowstone. When they arrived at home, Ngan's dad said they had driven 2,163 miles. What was the distance from Roosevelt National Park to Kansas City?

B. In Badlands National Park they hiked a total of 18.5 kilometers. The Roberts Prairie Dog Town trail was 7.5 kilometers each way. How long was the Saddle Pass Trail?

C. In Yellowstone, Ngan's family kept count of the animals they saw. The first day they saw three moose and two big horn sheep. The next day they saw a coyote and a herd of 125 bison. While driving around that day they saw a lot of elk. The total number of animals seen on the first two days was 163. How many elk did they see?

D. Ngan bought a postcard at each stop to make a scrapbook for her trip. The scrapbook cost her $5.89, the glue stick and pens to write in the scrapbook cost $1.75. She spent a total of $11.97 on all the supplies and postcards. How much did she spend on postcards?

Math Logic & Word Problems • 5–6 © 2005 Creative Teaching Press

The Aquarium

Max and Jenna are buying an aquarium. They have decided on a large 50-gallon aquarium and now need to buy the accessories and fish to outfit the tank.

A. The aquarium needs 1 pound of gravel for each gallon of water. If the gravel is sold in bags of 5 pounds and Max and Jenna buy 2 cases of gravel, how many bags are in a case?

B. The store has 61 guppies divided into 8 aquarium tanks, and a small display aquarium on the sales counter. Each of the 8 tanks has an even number in them with the remaining guppies in the display aquarium. How many guppies are in each aquarium and in the display aquarium?

C. The store also has 52 Mollies. These are divided by color in 12 aquarium tanks, with the remaining Mollies in the display tank on the sales counter. There is an equal number of Mollies in each color group. How many Mollies are in each aquarium and in the display aquarium?

D. The display tank contains guppies, Mollies, and tetras. There is a total of 13 fish in the display tank. Use the calculations from B and C to find out how many tetras are in the tank.

E. Max and Jenna have decided to buy 30 fish. Max picked out 9 guppies and Jenna found 13 Mollies she liked. How many tetras can they buy?

Math Logic & Word Problems • 5–6 © 2005 Creative Teaching Press

Name _____ Date _____

Guess How Many

SHOW ME THE WAY

A. Brenna and her family moved to Ohio. The first week she wrote some letters and postcards to send to friends back in Nebraska. She spent $2.54 on postage. If it cost $0.37 to send a letter and $0.23 to send a postcard, how many of each did she send to her friends?

Strategic Steps

1 There are a couple of ways to solve this problem. The first is to estimate and divide, then check your work and adjust your guess from there.

2 30 cents will go into $2.50 about 8 times. Try 4 letters at $0.37 and 4 postcards at $0.23.

$$(4 \times \$0.37) + (4 \times \$0.23) = \underline{\hspace{2cm}}$$

3 From that answer adjust your guesses by increasing either the letters or postcards and reducing the others to see how many of each will equal $2.54 in postage.

B. Kate and Neha went to the park and met some other friends; they were all watching some ants. Between the friends and the ants, there were 30 legs. How many people and how many ants could there have been?

Strategic Steps

1 Use some things you know to make an estimate. You know that people have 2 legs and that ants have 6 legs. Five ants would have 30 legs, so you know the number is less than that.

2 Make an estimate on the number of people and the number of ants. Check it and if needed, change your estimate and try again.

$$(\underline{\hspace{1.5cm}} \times 2) + (\underline{\hspace{1.5cm}} \times 6) = \underline{\hspace{2cm}}$$

Summer Trips

A. Bontu went to the store and bought a dozen pieces of fruit. Each apple cost $0.27, and each orange cost $0.45. He spent $3.96. How many oranges and how many apples did he buy?

B. Wendy's family went on a horseback trip. All together there were 72 legs. How many people and how many horses were on the trip?

C. Bontu's family set up camp using pup tents. Each tent had 2 poles and 6 stakes. All together there were 48 poles and stakes. How many tents did they set up?

D. In the campground parking lot there were twice as many cars as motorcycles. All together there were 30 wheels. How many cars and motorcycles were there?

Ready for School

A. Samantha bought pencils and erasers for school. She bought a total of 30 items costing $3.78. If a pencil cost $0.12 and an eraser cost $0.15, how many of each did she buy?

B. Leanne signed her new puppy up for obedience classes. There were a total of 40 bodies in the class with 116 legs. How many were puppies and how many were people?

C. At lunch, 50 children bought either chocolate or white milk. Chocolate milk costs $0.30 and white milk costs $0.25. The total cost of the milk sold was $13.30. How many chocolate milks and white milks were sold?

D. Qushawn was one of the first students into the classroom. When he arrived there were 44 people and chairs in the room with a total of 152 legs. How many people were in the room?

Math Logic & Word Problems • 5–6 © 2005 Creative Teaching Press

Implied Steps

SHOW ME THE WAY

A. Kamau's mom drives 24 miles each way to work. She works 5 days a week. How many miles will she drive in a month?

Strategic Steps

This problem looks simple but it is asking for several steps that are not specifically identified.

1 The problem says that she drove 24 miles each way to work. Since she goes to work (24 miles) and then comes home (another 24 miles), how many miles is she driving a day?

$$24 \times 2 = \text{_____} \text{ miles driven per day}$$

2 Next, you would calculate the weekly mileage (you are given that she works 5 days each week).

$$\text{_____ (miles per day)} \times 5 = \text{_____ miles driven per week}$$

3 The problem asks how many miles she drives in a month. For this you will need to know that there are typically 4 weeks in a month.

$$\text{_____ (miles per week)} \times 4 = \text{_____ miles driven per month}$$

B. Melanie and her 4 friends are all working 2 hours per school day to earn money for a school band trip. The girls are making $5 per hour. How much money will they earn in 2 months? Show the number sentence for each item.

Hours worked each week   _____   _____

Amount made per week   _____   _____

Amount made per month   _____   _____

Amount made over 2-month time _____   _____

Math Logic & Word Problems • 5–6 © 2005 Creative Teaching Press

Summer Vacation

Allison, Roger, and Nathan spent the summer with their grandparents on the family farm. They had lots of adventures and helped with the farming chores.

A. Allison helped her grandfather pick corn to sell at the farmers' market every day during July. Each day they were able to pick 15 dozen ears of corn. Then they would drive to the farmers' market and sell the corn for $4 per dozen.
How much money did they make that month?

Amount made per day _____

Amount made in July _____

B. Nathan helped by watering the herb garden. Each afternoon and evening he would carry 5 gallons of water to sprinkle on the garden. How much water did he carry during the month of August?

Amount of water per day _____

Water carried during August _____

C. Roger would ride his bicycle to deliver eggs and milk to his uncle's house, 2 miles away from the farm. He made this delivery every day in July. How many miles did Roger ride on his deliveries during that month?

Distance per day _____

Distance in July _____

Music Lessons

A. Cyrus was taking cello lessons. He practiced for 1 hour every morning and then another hour every evening, every day of the week. How many hours did he practice each month?

Hours practiced per day   _____

Hours practiced per week   _____

Hours practiced per month _____

B. Elana wanted to take clarinet lessons. Each lesson would cost $12 and she would take lessons twice a week. How much would 6 months worth of lessons cost?

Cost of lessons per week   _____

Cost of lessons per month   _____

Cost of lessons for 6 months _____

C. Abe had been taking piano lessons for a year. He estimated he practiced one hour per day every day for a year. In addition, he took lessons for 2 hours per week. How many hours did he play the piano during that year?

Hours practiced in a year   _____

Hours taking lessons per week   _____

Hours taking lessons per month   _____

Hours taking lessons per year   _____

Hours spent playing the
piano during the year   _____

Math Logic & Word Problems • 5–6 © 2005 Creative Teaching Press

Fraction Puzzles

Show Me the Way

A. Using the numbers 3, 4, 8, and 8 fill in the spaces below to form two fractions that add up as close to one as possible.

$$\underline{\quad} + \underline{\quad} = \underline{\quad}$$

Strategic Steps

1 Since 8 is the one number that is repeated, use it as the denominator for both fractions.

2 Use the other numbers as numerators, then complete the addition sentence.

B. Using the numbers 7, 8, and 15 fill in the empty spaces below to make fractions that complete the subtraction sentence to have the lowest possible number.

$$\frac{\underline{\quad}}{15} - \underline{\quad} = \underline{\quad}$$

Hint: As you did in the first problem, fill in the denominators first, and then set up the numerators so that you will have the lowest possible number.

Fraction Sums and Differences

A. Use each of the numbers 2 and 3 twice to fill in the spaces with proper fractions to create a number sentence with a sum that is greater than 1.

$$\frac{\quad}{\quad} + \frac{\quad}{\quad} = \frac{\quad}{\quad} =$$

B. Use the numbers 3, 9, 12, and 12 to fill in the spaces to create a fraction subtraction sentence that results in a fraction that can be reduced to ½.

$$\frac{\quad}{\quad} - \frac{\quad}{\quad} = \frac{\quad}{\quad} = \frac{1}{2}$$

C. Use the numbers 13, 17, 21, and 21 to fill in the spaces to create a number sentence with a sum that is less than 2.

$$\frac{\quad}{\quad} + \frac{\quad}{\quad} = \frac{\quad}{\quad} =$$

D. Use the numbers 2, 8, 9 and 9 to fill in the spaces to create a fraction subtraction sentence that results in a fraction that is less than 1 but greater than ½.

$$\frac{\quad}{\quad} - \frac{\quad}{\quad} = \frac{\quad}{\quad} = \frac{\quad}{\quad}$$

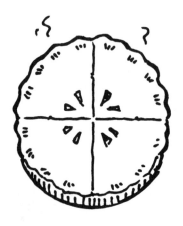
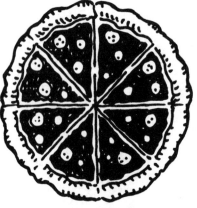

Math Logic & Word Problems • 5–6 © 2005 Creative Teaching Press

Fraction Addition and Subtraction

Use the information given to form fractions with unlike denominators into true addition and subtraction statements.

A. Use the numbers 1, 2, 3, and 6 to fill in the spaces to form two fractions that add up to the number one.

$$\frac{\quad}{\quad} + \frac{\quad}{\quad} = 1$$

B. Use the numbers 4, 6, 10, and 12 to fill in the spaces to form two proper fractions that will add up to a fraction greater than one.

$$\frac{\quad}{\quad} + \frac{\quad}{\quad} = \frac{\quad}{\quad} =$$

C. Use the numbers 2, 6, 8, and 12 to fill in the spaces to form two proper fractions that will form a subtraction sentence that equals ⅓.

$$\frac{\quad}{\quad} - \frac{\quad}{\quad} = \frac{1}{3}$$

D. Use the numbers 3, 6, 20, and 24 to fill in the spaces to form two proper fractions that will have the lowest possible answer.

$$\frac{\quad}{\quad} - \frac{\quad}{\quad} = \frac{\quad}{\quad} =$$

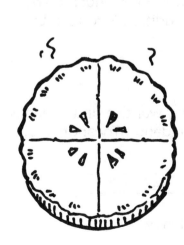  

Name _____ Date _____

 # Can You Guess?

SHOW ME THE WAY

A. You have 15 coins that total $1.34. You have the same number of dimes and quarters, 1 more penny than dimes, and 1 more nickel than pennies. What coins do you have?

Strategic Steps

1 First, you know that there is a minimum of 4 pennies. That leaves $1.30 to find.

2 Since there is 1 more penny than dimes, that means there are 3 dimes. You also have the same number of dimes and quarters, so you have 3 quarters.

$3 \times \$0.10 =$ _____ $3 \times \$0.25 =$ _____

3 You know you have one more nickel than pennies, so you would have _____ nickels.

_____ $\times \$0.05 =$ _____

4 Add all the amounts together and see if they add up to $1.34.

B. The sum of two numbers is 26 and their product is 168. What are the two numbers?

Strategic Steps

1 Start by listing some of the numbers that will add up to 26. Since the product is large, that tells you the numbers will be large. Try 10 + 16 = 26. The addition is correct, but if you multiply the numbers what product will you get?

$16 \times 10 =$ _____

2 Is that number higher or lower than 168? If it is higher, you may want to find addends where one is lower. If it is lower, you may want to use larger addends. Try another set of numbers.

_____ + _____ = 26   _____ $\times$ _____ = _____

3 Continue trying numbers until you find the correct pair of addends.

Math Logic & Word Problems • 5–6 © 2005 Creative Teaching Press

Your Guess, Please

A. At the zoo, you see a combination of bison and sandhill cranes at a pond. Together, there are 21 animals and a total of 58 legs. How many animals are cranes and how many are bison?

B. Steph has $30.00 to go shopping for clothing. She finds several items on sale. If a blouse costs $10.99, pants cost $12.99, a sweater costs $9.99, and a T-shirt costs $8.99, which three items of clothing can she buy for $30.00?

C. There are two numbers whose product is 117 and quotient is 13. What are the two numbers?

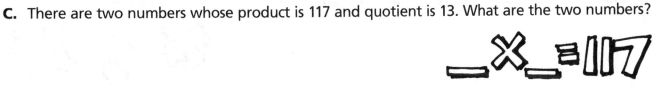

D. Maggie buys some packs of vegetable seeds to plant. She buys a pack of 35 corn seeds, a pack of 57 lima beans seeds, a pack of 54 watermelon seeds, and a pack of 30 pea seeds. That afternoon she plants two packets with a total of 89 seeds. Which two vegetables did she plant?

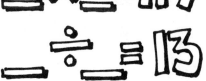

Can You Double-Check That?

A. On Bring-Your-Pet-to-School Day, 14 classmates brought in birds and dogs. When added together, the pets had 36 legs. How many pets were dogs? How many were birds?

B. You have 11 coins that total 43 cents. What combination of coins can you have?

C. There are two numbers whose sum is 25 and product is 156. What are the two numbers?

D. Forest and Emil were comparing the number of baseball cards they have. Together they have 20 cards. The product of the two numbers is 96. Forest has more cards than Emil. How many cards does each boy have?

Math Logic & Word Problems • 5–6 © 2005 Creative Teaching Press

Name _____ Date _____

The Game

SHOW ME THE WAY

A. The Knights were having a wonderful basketball season. The scores were 86, 92, 64, 85, 48, 96, and 76. What is their average score rounded to the nearest whole number?

Strategic Steps

❶ First, add all the numbers.

$$86 + 92 + 64 + 85 + 48 + 96 + 76 = \text{_____}$$

❷ Divide that sum by the number of items added, in this case 7.

$$\text{_____} \div 7 = \text{_____}$$

B. Mariah joined the track team at school. She needed to run an average of 4 kilometers a day to get ready for the first track meet. This week, she averaged 4.3 kilometers per day, but forgot to record the number of kilometers she ran on Wednesday. Figure out how many kilometers Mariah ran on Wednesday.

Day	Distance
Monday	3.7 km
Tuesday	4.2 km
Wednesday	
Thursday	4.8 km
Friday	5.2 km
Saturday	5.1 km
Sunday	3.3 km

Strategic Steps

❶ Since you know the average for 7 days is 4.3 kilometers per day, the first step is to multiply that times 7 to find the total distance ran during the week.

$$4.3 \times 7 = \text{_____} \text{ (total distance ran)}$$

❷ Now, add up all the numbers you have. That number is _____.

❸ Subtract that number from the total distance ran.

$$\underbrace{\text{_____}}_{\text{(total distance ran)}} - \underbrace{\text{_____}}_{\text{(distance ran other days)}} = \text{_____ distance ran on Wednesday}$$

Name _____ Date _____

Veterinarian Clinic

A. Amanda was helping at the veterinarian clinic, and she weighed the cats that had been examined that day. The cats weighed 8.2, 9.7, 12.4, 6.9, 8.2, 7.8, 9.4, 8.9, 6.5, and 11.4 pounds. What is the average weight of the cats?

B. The veterinarian asked Amanda to find out the average number of dogs seen over the past year. Amanda checked the records and found this data: January, 372; February, 298; March, 446; April, 322; May, 400; June, 428; July, 403; August, 312; September, 288; October, 332; November, 397; December, 251. What is the monthly average of dogs seen in the veterinarian clinic?

C. On Saturday, Amanda was asked to organize a birthday lunch for the receptionist. Of the six employees who contributed, each gave an average of $6.75 for lunch. Dr. Samson gave $10.00, Dr. Williams gave $8.00, Amanda gave $3.50, and the two veterinarian technicians gave $5.00 each. Dr. Soto made up the difference. How much did she pay?

Math Logic & Word Problems • 5–6 © 2005 Creative Teaching Press

Name _____ Date _____

Jobs

A. Sean spent his snow day from school going around the neighborhood shoveling driveways. He shoveled five driveways taking 90 minutes, 60 minutes, 45 minutes, 110 minutes, and 75 minutes to do the jobs. What was the average time to shovel one driveway?

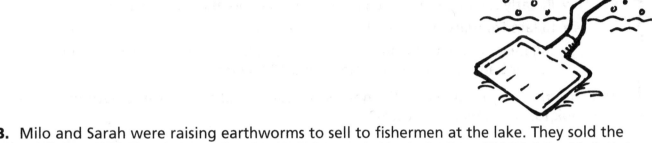

B. Milo and Sarah were raising earthworms to sell to fishermen at the lake. They sold the following amounts each weekend day during the month: 14 dozen; 18 dozen; 22 dozen; 8 dozen; 15 dozen; 15 dozen; 28 dozen; and 6 dozen. What was the average number of earthworms Milo and Sarah sold each day?

C. Delia has been working for several families babysitting over the past week. She earned an average of $20 per night for four nights. On Monday she earned $15, on Saturday she earned $25, and on Sunday she earned $20. How much did she earn on Friday night?

D. Xavier is collecting aluminum cans for recycling. Each Saturday for nine weeks he took cans to the recycling center. These are the weights of the cans he recycled: 38 pounds; 42 pounds; 58 pounds; 71 pounds; 36 pounds; 23 pounds; 41 pounds; and 65 pounds. He averaged 50 pounds per week. He noticed he was missing one week's weight of cans. Help him find the missing weight.

Math Logic & Word Problems • 5–6 © 2005 Creative Teaching Press

Checkbook Math

Show Me the Way

Julianna opened her first checking account. She had $150.00 that her grandparents sent her for Christmas.

- In early January she spent $127.85 on new toys and video games.
- In late February she spent $29.35 for a birthday present for her mother.
- Julianna got a letter from the bank stating that she had overdrawn her account and they were charging her a $20.00 fee.

How much money (rounded to the nearest $5.00) will Julianna have to earn to pay the bank for the amount she owes?

Date	Description of transaction	Debit	Deposit	Balance

Strategic Steps

1. On each line of the checkbook register enter a description of the transaction. Label each with a "+" sign for additions and a "−" sign for subtractions.

2. After each entry, either add or subtract the amount to keep a running total.

3. Enter the fee to get the total negative amount.

4. Round that figure to the nearest $5.00 to find how much money Julianna needs to earn to cover the negative balance.

Math Logic & Word Problems • 5–6 © 2005 Creative Teaching Press

Yard Work

Bryan has his first job. He is helping his neighbor with yard work. Every Saturday morning he goes over and helps pull up dandelions, pull weeds from the flower beds, pick up any sticks that fall off trees, and rake up any leaves or other debris on the lawn. His neighbor is paying him $10.00 every week.

Bryan saved most of his money for the first two months, and on April 12 he opened a checking account with $76.50.

Date	Description of transaction	Debit	Deposit	Balance
4/12	Opened checking account			76.50

- On April 14, he wrote a check for $50.00 to pay for swim lessons.

- On April 16, he bought a new swimsuit for $22.64.

- On April 18, he deposited $10.00.

- On April 22, he bought new swim goggles and flippers for $14.95.

- On April 24, he got a letter from the bank stating he had overdrawn his account and was being charged $20.00.

If Bryan deposits the $10.00 he earned that Saturday, what would his balance be?

_____

Mistakes

Sean had been adding and subtracting deposits and checks from his checking account for over a year and every month his balance was the same as the balance on the bank statement. But this month something must have gone wrong.

Checkbook Register

Date	Description of transaction	Debit	Deposit	Balance
6/20	Balance			23.76
6/21	Deposit		+25.00	48.76
	Music Store	−22.98		25.78
	Toy Store	−14.23		21.55
	Deposit		+16.00	35.55
7/7	Department Store	−32.14		3.41
7/8	Deposit		+25.00	28.41

Complete the bank statement to help him find his mistakes.

Bank Statement

Date	Description of transaction	Debit	Deposit	Balance
6/20	Balance			23.76
6/21	Deposit		+25.00	
	Music Store	−22.98		
	Toy Store	−14.23		
	Deposit		+16.00	
7/7	Department Store	−32.14		
	Bank fee for negative balance	−20.00		
7/8	Deposit		+25.00	

What mistakes did Sean make? _____

_____

_____

Math Logic & Word Problems • 5–6 © 2005 Creative Teaching Press

Name _____ Date _____

First Jobs

SHOW ME THE WAY

A. Kyong took over his brother's paper route. Every month, he collected $612.00 from his customers. Out of that he had to pay $367.20 to the newspaper company for the papers; the rest was his to keep. Every month, he deposits $150.00 into a college savings account, and he keeps $50.00 for necessities. If he does all this, how long will it take him to save $186.75 for the new bicycle he wants to buy?

Strategic Steps

1 This is easiest if you first add all the money Kyong wants to spend (or deposit in his savings account).

To newspaper company	$367.20
College savings	150.00
Spending money	50.00
Total	$567.20

2 Now, subtract this total from the money collected from his customers.

$612.00 – _____ = _____ (money left each month)

3 The next step is to divide this into $186.75 (cost of new bicycle) and round up to the next even month.

$186.75 ÷ _____ (money left each month) = _____ (months to save for bicycle)

B. Hunter went to the store for his mother. He bought three loaves of bread at $1 each, two gallons of milk at $2 each, and two boxes of cereal at $4 each. How much change would he get from a $20 bill?

Strategic Steps

1 First, add up the cost of all the items.

(3 × $1) + (2 × $2) + (2 × $4) = _____ (cost of items)

2 Next, subtract that from the amount paid.

$20 – _____ (cost of items) = _____ (change)

Math Logic & Word Problems • 5–6 © 2005 Creative Teaching Press

Earning and Spending

A. Satara is helping her neighbor by walking her three dogs. She is paid $1.50 per dog each day. She walks the dogs every day except Sunday. Satara wants to save $25.00 per month for college. She wants to take swim lessons for $34.75 per month, and then have $5.00 per week spending money. She wants to use any remaining money to buy a new skateboard for $84.50. Assuming there are four weeks in a month, how long will it take Satara to save for the skateboard?

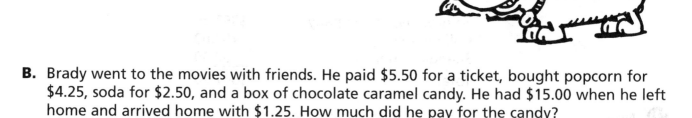

B. Brady went to the movies with friends. He paid $5.50 for a ticket, bought popcorn for $4.25, soda for $2.50, and a box of chocolate caramel candy. He had $15.00 when he left home and arrived home with $1.25. How much did he pay for the candy?

C. Nellie earned $340 doing odd jobs over the summer. She earned $175 babysitting, $50 pet sitting, $25 running errands, and the rest from mowing lawns. How much did she earn mowing lawns?

Math Logic & Word Problems • 5–6 © 2005 Creative Teaching Press

How Long?

A. Three days a week, after school, Lauren works in her uncle's grocery store and helps to prepare empty cardboard boxes for recycling. Her uncle pays her $10 a day for helping. Lauren wants to save $540 to buy a round trip ticket to fly to her grandmother's house for the summer. If she saves all her earnings, how many weeks will it take to save the money for the ticket?

B. Francis went to a yard sale and picked out several items. He found six books for $0.25 each; a box of baseball cards for $0.75; a new basketball for $1.50; a box of doll clothes for his little sister for $1.25, and two T-shirts for $0.50 each. He handed the lady a $10.00 bill. How much change did he get?

C. Ruthann wanted to earn enough money to buy a new bookcase that costs $85. She has a job babysitting every Friday night for four hours. She makes $4 per hour babysitting. Her parents have agreed to give her $10 per week if she would wash both their cars on Saturday. How many weeks will it take her to save enough to buy the bookcase?

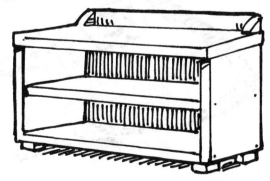

Math Logic & Word Problems • 5–6 © 2005 Creative Teaching Press

Jelly Beans

SHOW ME THE WAY

Bryan and Andy bought a bag of jelly beans and told their brother, Warren, that he could have the jelly beans if he could tell them how many were in the bag. They gave him the following clues:

- There are more than 80 jelly beans but less than 100 jelly beans.

- You can divide the jelly beans equally into groups of 3.

- If you divide the jelly beans into groups of 5, there will be 2 left over.

How many jelly beans are there?

Strategic Steps

1 The first clue gives you a range where the correct number is located. Write the possible numbers in that range here:

_____

2 The second clue tells you that the number is a multiple of 3. Cross out the numbers in step 1 that are not multiples of 3.

3 The third clue tells you that the number is 2 more than a multiple of 5. Look at the remaining numbers. Which one of those numbers is 2 more than a multiple of 5?

_____

Math Logic & Word Problems • 5–6 © 2005 Creative Teaching Press

Name _____ Date _____

The Penny Jar

Wendy found a small jar with pennies and counted them, and then challenged her brother Craig to guess how many pennies she had. She gave him some clues to help out:

• The number of pennies is between 70 and 100. You can divide the pennies equally into groups of 5.

• If you divide the pennies into groups of 4, there will be 3 pennies left over.

• If you divide the pennies into groups of 6 or 9, there will be 5 left over.

• If you divide the pennies into groups of 10, there will be 5 left over.

How many pennies are in the jar? Show how you found your answer.

Marbles

Michael and Carly found a bag of marbles in Grandma's attic. Michael counted them and gave Carly the following clues to guess how many marbles are in the bag:

- There are more than 150 marbles, but less than 170.

- You can divide the marbles equally into two, three, or six groups.

- If you divide the marbles into five groups, there will be 2 left over.

- If you divide the marbles into four groups, there will be 2 left over.

How many marbles are in the bag?

Math Logic & Word Problems • 5–6 © 2005 Creative Teaching Press

Let's Double

SHOW ME THE WAY

Mrs. Bartee was given two bromeliads as a Christmas gift one year. Bromeliads are very interesting plants. The parent plant will bloom once in a lifetime and then will produce two "pups" or small plants that grow at the base of the parent. The parent will die and the two smaller plants will grow. This way, the plants will double in number every year. The following chart shows what happened to the bromeliads over the first few years.

Year	Number of Plants
1	2
2	4
3	8
4	16
5	

Year	Number of Plants
6	
7	
8	
9	
10	

How many plants will be in the class at the end of ten years? Make a prediction and then work to see if you are right. How close are the calculations and your prediction?

Strategic Steps

1 Use the information given in the chart to predict how many plants there will be after the next six years. Write down that prediction.

_____

2 Now, continue the chart to show exactly what happens during those six years. Each year the number of plants will double. Use the blank chart to record your work.

3 Compare your prediction and the number you calculated. How close were you?

_____

_____

Science Experiment

Lina and Courtney are raising a colony of amoebae as part of their science project. To reproduce, an amoeba will divide into two parts, forming two new amoebae. Each generation will double the number of amoebae.

Courtney and Lina are trying to estimate how many amoebae they will have in 10 generations if they start with 5 amoebae. Here is the data they have collected from the first few generations.

Generation	Number of Amoebae
1	5
2	10
3	20
4	40
5	

Generation	Number of Amoebae
6	
7	
8	
9	
10	

Predict how many amoebae there will be after 10 generations. _____

Fill in the charts and find out how many amoebae there are after 10 generations.

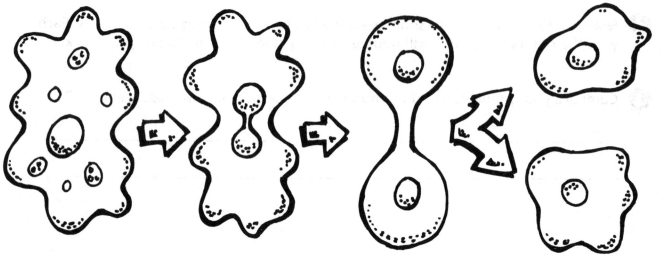

Math Logic & Word Problems • 5–6 © 2005 Creative Teaching Press

Name _____ Date _____

Charlotte's Decision

Charlotte was collecting money for a charity walk with her class. Her father offered to give her either $25 or 1 penny doubled every day for 14 days. Which should she choose?

Make a chart or diagram to show how much a penny doubled every day for 14 days would equal.

Math Logic & Word Problems • 5–6 © 2005 Creative Teaching Press

Reading Contest

SHOW ME THE WAY

Margaret, Betty, Chalondra, and Pete all entered the class' reading contest. Together, they read 96 pages.

- Pete read ³⁄₁₂ the total pages.
- Betty read 12 fewer pages than Pete.
- Chalondra read 18 more pages than Pete.
- Margaret read 6 more pages than Betty.

How many pages did each student read?

Pete _____   Chalondra _____

Betty _____   Margaret _____

Strategic Steps

① Pete read ³⁄₁₂ of the total pages. To find the number of pages that he read, you need to multiply ³⁄₁₂ by 96.

$$\frac{3}{12} \times 96 = \underline{\hspace{2cm}} \text{ (pages that Pete read)}$$

② To find the number of pages that Betty read, you take the number of pages that Pete read and then subtract 12 pages.

_____ (pages that Pete read) − 12 = _____ (pages that Betty read)

③ Chalondra read 18 more pages than Pete.

_____ (pages that Pete read) + 18 = _____ (pages that Chalondra read)

④ Margaret read 6 more pages than Betty.

_____ (pages that Betty read) + 6 = _____ (pages that Margaret read)

⑤ To check your work, add up the pages that all the students read. The answer should be 96.

Math Logic & Word Problems • 5–6 © 2005 Creative Teaching Press

Basketball Game

The Monarchs made 112 points in the final basketball game of the season.

- Jethro made ⅝ of those points.

- Peter made 58 points less than Jethro.

- Jack made half as many points as Peter.

- Max made ⅛ of the points.

- Forrest made 4 more points than Jack.

How many points did each boy score?

Jethro _____

Peter _____

Jack _____

Max _____

Forrest _____

Math Logic & Word Problems • 5–6 © 2005 Creative Teaching Press

Tulips

Cameron and Fiona live in a town that celebrates its Dutch heritage by planting large numbers of tulip bulbs in the fall so that the town will come alive with color in the spring. The children planted bulbs for 9 days.

- The children are given a box of 300 tulip bulbs. They were so excited that when they got home on Friday, they planted 12 bulbs in their yard.

- On Saturday they planted ⅛ of the remaining bulbs along the sidewalk in front of their house.

- On Sunday, with the help of their parents, they planted 14 more than they did on Saturday.

- On Monday, Tuesday, Wednesday, and Thursday, Cameron and Fiona each planted 15 bulbs.

- On Friday, with the help of school friends, they planted 10 more than Cameron and Fiona planted on Saturday.

- On Saturday, Cameron and Fiona finished planting the bulbs and planted as many as they had the previous Saturday.

How many bulbs did the friends plant each day?

Math Logic & Word Problems • 5–6 © 2005 Creative Teaching Press

Venn Diagram

SHOW ME THE WAY

There are 22 students in your class. Eleven students are taking swimming lessons. Some students are taking gymnastics. Eight of the students are taking both swimming and gymnastics. How many students are taking only gymnastics?

Strategic Steps

1 One solution to this problem would be to draw a Venn diagram to help organize the data. Start by drawing two circles that are overlapping.

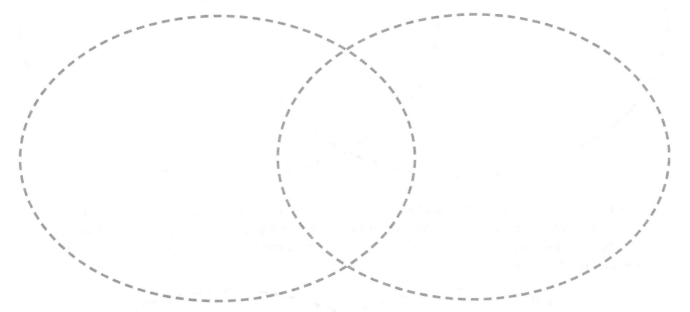

2 Label one circle swimming and one circle gymnastics. The overlapping section is for students who are taking both swimming and gymnastics.

3 You can find the number of students taking only gymnastics by adding the number who are taking only swimming lessons and those who are taking both, then subtracting this number from the total number of students. There are 15 students taking swimming lessons and 8 students taking both swimming and gymnastics. Add those two numbers.

$$11 + 8 = _____$$

4 Now, subtract that number from the total number of students in the class.

$$22 - _____ = _____$$ (number of students taking only gymnastics)

Gymnastics Challenges

A. There are 26 boys on the gymnastics team who work with either the parallel bars or rings. Twelve students work on the parallel bars and four students work with both parallel bars and rings. How many students work only on rings? Use the Venn diagram to solve this problem.

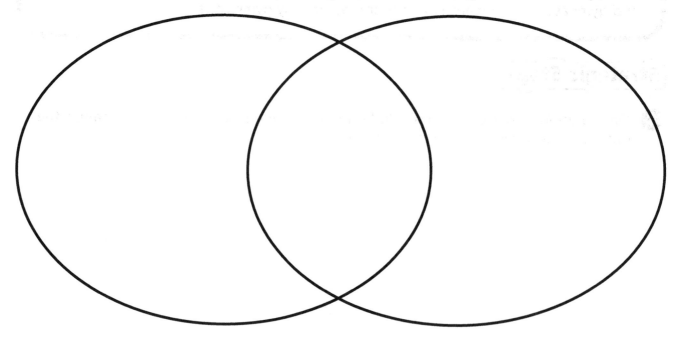

B. The girls' gymnastics team works on either the uneven bars or balance beam. There are eight students who work only on the uneven bars. Six students work only on the balance beam. Two girls work on both the uneven bars and balance beam. How many students are on the gymnastics team?

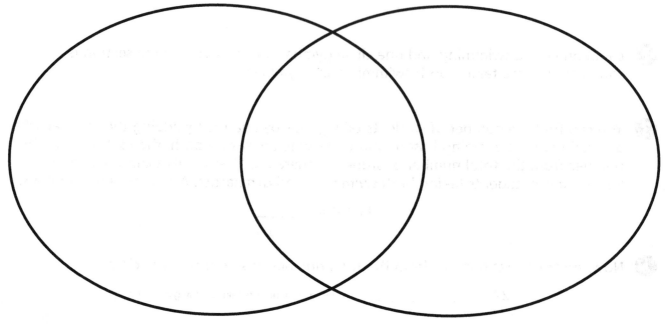

Math Logic & Word Problems • 5–6 © 2005 Creative Teaching Press

More Diagrams

A. Ruthann took a survey of fifth graders to find out which ones like to jump rope or play on the monkey bars at recess. She found that 15 students like to jump rope and 17 students like to play on the monkey bars. An additional 7 students like to do both. How many students are in her class? Draw a diagram to help you solve this problem.

B. Your school is trying to pick a new mascot. The choices are panther or tiger. Altogether, 75 students voted for panthers, tigers, or both. A total of 28 students voted just for panthers, and 12 students liked both the panther and the tiger. How many voted just for tigers? Draw a diagram to help you solve this problem.

Who Is First?

SHOW ME THE WAY

Hannah, Mike, Rachel, Matthew, and Emma are standing in line for lunch. Use the following clues to list the order of the four friends.

- Hannah is in front of Mike.
- Rachel is behind Mike.
- Matthew is heading up the group.
- Emma is behind Hannah but before Mike.

Strategic Steps

(Note: This is only one strategy. There are other ways to solve this problem.)

1 Draw a diagram showing the five places in line.

2 The third clue tells us that Matthew is heading up the group, so he would be first in line.

3 The first clue tells us that Hannah is in front of Mike and the second clue tells us that Rachel is behind Mike. The fourth clue tells us that Emma is also before Mike, so that leaves only Rachel to be the last in line.

4 The fourth clue tells us that Emma is behind Hannah but before Mike. That gives us the order Hannah, Emma, then Mike. Hannah would be second in line followed by Emma then Mike.

Which Floor?

Five classmates—Nadia, Carol, Mario, Kai, and Bailey live in the same apartment building.

- When Nadia visits Carol, she has to go down 2 floors.

- Mario lives on the floor between Kai and Carol.

- When Bailey goes to Nadia's to play, she goes up 1 floor.

- Kai lives on the first floor.

Which floor does each child live on?

Nadia _____

Carol _____

Mario _____

Kai _____

Bailey _____

Band Concert

Zane, Danny, Joey, Cassandra, Dominic, and Meagan were in line to buy tickets for the band concert.

• Danny is between Joey and Cassandra.

• Cassandra is behind Dominic.

• There are three people between Dominic and Meagan.

• Dominic has to look over Zane's shoulder to see the ticket booth.

Write the order that the six friends are standing in line.

Zane _____   Cassandra _____

Danny _____   Dominic _____

Joey _____   Meagan _____

Math Logic & Word Problems • 5–6 © 2005 Creative Teaching Press

Name _____ Date _____

Magic Squares

Show Me the Way

Magic squares have been around for hundreds of years. In reality, there is nothing "magic" about them. They are simply a pattern of numbers arranged in a manner where all rows or columns will add up to the same number. Each number will appear only once in a magic square.

4		2
3		
8	1	6

For the following magic square, fill in the missing numbers. All columns and rows will add up to 15. Do not use a number more than once or repeat a number already used.

Strategic Steps

1 The first known about this square is that all columns and rows will add up to 15. If you look at the top row, you are given the numbers 4 and 2. The first step is to add those together.

4 + 2 = _____   Subtract that sum from 15:   15 – _____ = _____

Use that number to fill in the blank square in the top row.

2 The second row is more difficult because it has two blanks. Instead of the second row, look at the second column. You have determined that _____ is the missing number in the first row, so add that to the 1 from the third row.

_____ + 1 = _____   Subtract that sum from 15:   15 – _____ = _____

Put that number in the middle square.

3 Finally, you need to find the middle number of the third column. You know that the given numbers are 2 and 6.

2 + 6 = _____   Subtract that sum from 15:   15 – _____ = _____

Put that number in the remaining blank square.

4 To check your work, add up the numbers in all the columns and then in the rows to make sure they each equal 15.

Could It Be Magic?

Magic squares have been around for hundreds of years. In reality there is nothing magic about them. They are simply a pattern of numbers arranged in a manner where all rows or columns will add up to the same number. Each number will only appear once in a magic square.

This magic square has all columns and rows adding up to 21.
Fill in the missing numbers.

10		
3	7	
		4

This magic square has all columns and rows adding up to 34.
Fill in the missing numbers.

16		2	
		11	8
	6		
4	15	14	

Math Logic & Word Problems • 5–6 © 2005 Creative Teaching Press

Math Magic

Magic squares have been around for hundreds of years. In reality there is nothing magic about them. They are simply a pattern of numbers arranged in a manner where all rows or columns will add up to the same number. Each number will only appear once in a magic square.

This magic square has all columns and rows adding up to 34. Fill in the missing numbers.

1		11	
	13	2	
		16	9
15	10	5	4

This magic square has all columns and rows adding up to 80. It also uses only odd numbers between 5 and 35. (Hint: Write out the odd numbers in that range and cross each off as you use it.) Fill in the missing numbers.

33	15		9
	5	29	
13	35		
7			31

Prizes

SHOW ME THE WAY

A new toy store was opening in Chester on Saturday and all the children were very excited. Not only was the store having a sale on their favorite toys, but every child who visited the store got a balloon. Every 8th child will get a copy of a book. Every 40th child will get a card game. Every 80th child will get a copy of the newest movie release.

The newspaper predicts that 2,000 children will visit the store on opening day.

A. How many books, games, and movies will they give out?

B. How many children will get both a book and a game?

C. How many children will get all three prizes?

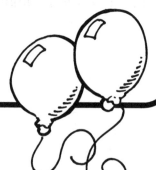

Strategic Steps

1 To solve this problem you need to find how many times each number will divide into 2,000. This will tell you:

$$2,000 \div 8 = _____ \qquad 2,000 \div 40 = _____ \qquad 2,000 \div 80 = _____$$

2 To find the children who will receive both a book and a game, you need to find the smallest or least common multiple of both 8 and 40. What number is it?

_____

3 To find the children who received all three prizes, you need to find the smallest or least common multiple of all three. What number is it?

_____

Math Logic & Word Problems • 5–6 © 2005 Creative Teaching Press

Lockers

Mrs. Stevens was excited to be the principal of a brand new school. When she realized that the lockers would not arrive until a couple of weeks after school started, she planned a celebration for their arrival.

When the lockers arrived on September 9, she knew that she had to do something with 9s. She decided that in every 9th locker she would put in a school pencil. Since it was the 15th day of school, she put a pack of erasers in every 15th locker. And then she put a school notebook in every 150th locker because the school was on 150th Street.

There are 1,152 students in the school. Remember, to find the answers, find the common multiples of the two or three numbers.

A. How many students got a pencil? _____

An eraser? _____

A notebook? _____

B. How many students got both a pencil and an eraser?

C. How many students would get a pencil, an eraser, and a notebook?

| 121 | 122 | 123 | 124 | 125 | 126 | 127 | 128 | 129 | 130 | 131 | 132 | 133 | 134 |

All Aboard!

Everyone in town was very excited about the new engine the local train museum was getting. This would allow the museum to have more train rides through the local park. This was a year of celebration. It was the 75th anniversary of the museum. The new engine's number was 21.

To celebrate the new train engine, the engineer was going to give every 21st passenger a postcard of the train. Every 75th passenger would get a ticket for a free train ride later in the year. The train holds a total of 57 people.

The museum will offer a 45-minute ride starting on the hour. The first train will leave at 7:00 a.m. and the last train will leave at 6:00 p.m.

A. How many passengers will receive a postcard?

B. How many will receive a free ticket?

C. Will any receive both a postcard and ticket? How many? (Hint: Find the multiples of the numbers and numbers in common with them.)

Math Logic & Word Problems • 5–6 © 2005 Creative Teaching Press

Name _____ Date _____

What Is Missing?

SHOW ME THE WAY

A **variable** is a number that is replaced by a letter representing an unknown number. To find the value of the variable, you will use one of the mathematic operations (addition, subtraction, multiplication, or division) to isolate the variable on one side to find the value it represents.

A. A number multiplied by 5 equals 30. What is the number? _____

Strategic Steps

1 Set this up as a problem with a variable.

$$5x = 30$$

2 Now, solve by moving the numbers by different operations to find the value of x.

$$\frac{5x}{5} = \frac{30}{5} \qquad x = \_\_\_\_\_$$

Use the same method to find the missing number for each problem.

B. After dividing a group of pumpkins into 3 groups, each group has 4 pumpkins. How many pumpkins did you start with? _____

C. I multiply a number by 4 and I get 68. What number am I? _____

D. $\frac{x}{6} = 24$ $\qquad x = \_\_\_\_\_$ $\qquad\qquad 8x = 72$ $\qquad x = \_\_\_\_\_$

E. When you add 7 to me it equals 36. What number am I? _____

F. When you subtract 54 from me, it equals 27. What number am I? _____

Missing Numbers

A **variable** is a number that is replaced by a letter representing an unknown number. To find the value of the variable, you will use one of the mathematic operations (addition, subtraction, multiplication, or division) to isolate the variable on one side to find the value it represents.

A. A number multiplied by 8 equals 40. What is the number?

B. After dividing the tennis balls into 6 groups, each group had 8 balls. How many balls did you start with?

C. Five groups of a number equal 30. What number was multiplied?

D. $5x = 35$ $\qquad\qquad\qquad$ $4x = 64$

$9 \div x = 3$ $\qquad\qquad\qquad$ $28 - x = 6$

E. I multiply a number by 6 and the answer is 42. What is the number I multiplied?

F. I divide a number by 3 and the answer is 11. What number did I divide?

Math Logic & Word Problems • 5–6 © 2005 Creative Teaching Press

✗3? Something Is Missing ✗4?

A **variable** is a number that is replaced by a letter representing an unknown number. To find the value of the variable, you will use one of the mathematic operations (addition, subtraction, multiplication, or division) to isolate the variable on one side to find the value it represents.

A. A number multiplied by 12 equals 108. What number is it?

B. A number plus 14 equals 47. What number is it?

C. Jamila has divided her stuffed animals into 12 equal groups. Each group has 4 animals. How many animals did she have when she started?

D. $\frac{x}{2} = 34$ $\qquad\qquad\qquad$ $14x = 84$

$\qquad$ $\frac{58}{x} = 29$ $\qquad\qquad\qquad$ $35 - x = 8$

E. I multiply a number by 12 and the answer is 72. What is the number I multiplied?

F. I divide a number by 8 and the answer is 16. What number did I divide?

Function Junction

SHOW ME THE WAY

Today was the 3rd Annual Train Festival and Khaliq has been helping get things ready.

- Khaliq showed up and was surprised to see that all the numbers had been changed. Actually, every number in the train station was different.
- The sign now read "5th Annual Train Festival." The cost for the festival had been changed from $5 to $9.
- The only thing that hadn't changed was that lunch was scheduled for 1 p.m.

On the station sign the name had been changed from Main Street Station to "Function Junction." In addition, taped on the front door was a note that said, *"My job is to change numbers. If you can't find out what I am, I will keep changing numbers."* It was signed "Function Master." Written on the back of the note were several functions:

$$F = n + 4 \qquad F = 2n + 1 \qquad F = 2n - 1 \qquad F = 4n - 5$$

Can you help Khaliq find out which is the correct function?

Strategic Steps

1 Look at the numbers that have been changed. Is there a pattern?
Try entering a number into each function and see what works.

2 Try the first formula.

$$F = n + 4 \qquad \text{if } n = 3 \qquad F = 3 + 4 = \text{\_\_\_\_\_}$$

We know that the Function Master changed 3 to 5, so if that function does not equal 5, then try another one of the functions. If the number equals 5, then try another number to make sure it is the correct function.

$F = n + 4$

$F = 2n - 1$

$F = 2n + 1$

$F = 4n - 5$

Math Logic & Word Problems • 5–6 © 2005 Creative Teaching Press

What Happened?

Zack opened an e-mail from his friend, Joseph, titled "Help Me!" and was surprised to hear what his friend wrote.

The Function Master has attacked me and I can't solve his riddles. He won't leave until I identify his function. I can't call for help because every time I enter a number into my phone, he changes it.

If I enter a 5, it becomes a 7. A 7 becomes an 11.

Even my address has been changed. The correct address is 34 S. 72nd Street, and now everything reads 65 S. 141st Street.

The only number that hasn't changed is the 3 in my phone number.

I found a note taped to the front door that said, *"Hello. Your numbers have been changed. Any number you use will be changed. The only way to stop this is to solve the puzzle and tell me how the numbers are being changed."*

—*The Function Master*

On the back door there was another note:

> *Do you want a clue? Functions come and functions go, but these are my favorites:*
>
> $F = 2n + 1$
> $F = 3n + 6$
> $F = n + 6$
> $F = 2n - 3$
>
> *Good luck!*
>
> —*The Function Master*

Zack, please help!

Joseph

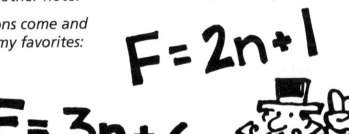

Help Zack find the function that the Function Master used.

Phone Numbers

Jaymin was surprised to discover the phone numbers in her phone directory have all been changed. Well not all, the number 1 is still there, but all other numbers are different.

- The emergency number 911 has become 25-1-1.

- Her grandmother's phone number is 529-2507 but now it reads:
  13-4-25 - 4-13-2-19

- All the other numbers have been changed.

Taped to the front of the phone directory is the message, *"You've been attacked by the Function Master. All your numbers went into my function machine and have been changed. The only way to change them back is to discover the function I used."*

Jaymin was so angry over the changed numbers she threw the phone directory across the room. Out fell a slip of paper that had been between the pages. It was another note:

I'm not completely heartless, I'm going to give you a clue. I like functions that multiply the original number by a single-digit integer and then subtract a different integer.

—The Function Master

Help Jaymin find the function.

Math Logic & Word Problems • 5–6 © 2005 Creative Teaching Press

Magician's Shapes

SHOW ME THE WAY

At Marvyn the Magician's show, Marvyn invited Elizabeth to be his assistant. Her job was to pick out a shape and place it in a black velvet bag for Marvyn to guess the shape. Marvyn would reach into the bag and would give out clues. See if you can put together the clues to help Marvyn guess the shape.

- This shape is 2-dimensional.
- The top and bottom lines are parallel.
- The corner angles are not right angles.
- There are 4 sides and all are of equal length.

Putting his fingers to his forehead with eyes closed, Marvyn is thinking of the shape's name. Can you help him?

Strategic Steps

1. Look at the clues Marvyn has given you. It is a flat shape and that rules out all the 3-dimensional shapes.

2. Parallel lines will rule out circles and ovals.

3. The fact the corners are not right angles will rule out squares and rectangles.

4. The 4 sides mean that it must be a quadrilateral of some type.

5. If all sides are equal, then there is only one type of quadrilateral that it could be: a _____.

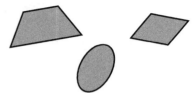

Marvyn's Shapes

At Marvyn the Magician's show, Marvyn invited Elizabeth to be his assistant. Her job was to pick out a shape and place it in a black velvet bag for Marvyn to guess the shape. Marvyn would reach into the bag and would give out clues. Put together the clues to help Marvyn guess the shapes.

A. "This shape is challenging," said Marvyn.

"This shape is a polyhedron."

"It has 6 faces and 12 edges."

Putting his fingers to his forehead with eyes closed,
Marvyn is thinking of the shape's name. What is the shape? _____

B. "One of my favorite shapes," said Marvyn.

"This shape is 2-dimensional and only has 3 corners."

"It has a right angle on one corner."

Putting his fingers to his forehead with eyes closed,
Marvyn is thinking of the shape's name. What is the shape? _____

C. "Ok, here's the last shape," said Marvyn.

"Another 2-dimensional shape for you."

"Hmmm… I feel curves."

"This has a longer side between the curved ends."

Putting his fingers to his forehead with eyes closed,
Marvyn is thinking of the shape's name. What is the shape? _____

Math Logic & Word Problems • 5–6 © 2005 Creative Teaching Press

Shape Magic

At Marvyn the Magician's show, Marvyn invited Elizabeth to be his assistant. Her job was to pick out a shape and place it in a black velvet bag for Marvyn to guess the shape. Marvyn would reach into the bag and would give out clues. Put together the clues to help Marvyn guess the shapes.

A. "Ahhh, I love a challenging shape," said Marvyn.

"Let me count the sides… 3, 4, 5, 6…"

"Oh, wait, here's 7 and 8."

Putting his fingers to his forehead with eyes closed,
Marvyn is thinking of the shape's name. What is the shape? _____

B. "Wow, this one is heavy," said Marvyn before he even put his hand in the bag.

"This one is long, slim, and definitely 3-dimensional."

"It is flat on top and round along the length."

Putting his fingers to his forehead with eyes closed,
Marvyn is thinking of the shape's name. What is the shape? _____

C. "This one is going to be easy, I just know it," he said as Elizabeth handed him the bag.

"I feel 4 sides on this flat shape."

"Two are parallel and the other two are sloping."

"The top parallel side is shorter than the bottom one."

Putting his fingers to his forehead with eyes closed,
Marvyn is thinking of the shape's name. What is the shape? _____

Circumference

SHOW ME THE WAY

Circumference is the distance around a circle. The formula for circumference is C = πd.

A. Marco is playing marbles and has drawn a circle with a circumference of 62.8 inches. How long is the diameter of the circle? Round your answer to the nearest whole number.

Strategic Steps

1 The formula for circumference is C = πd. The symbol π (pi) is a constant that equals 3.14.

2 Fill in the numbers you have and solve for d (diameter).

$$62.8 = 3.14(d) \qquad d = \frac{62.8}{3.14} \qquad d = \text{_____}$$

B. Daphne has set up the wading pool for her little sister to play in. She knows the radius of the pool is 36 inches. What is the circumference? Round your answer to the nearest whole number.

Strategic Steps

1 We know that the formula for circumference is C = πd. However, we don't know either the circumference or the diameter.

2 We do know that the diameter is twice the radius. So an alternative formula for circumference is C = 2πr.

3 Now, fill in the numbers you have and solve for C (circumference).

$$C = 2(3.14 \times 36 \text{ inches}) \qquad C = \text{_____} \text{ inches}$$

Math Logic & Word Problems • 5–6 © 2005 Creative Teaching Press

Name _____ Date _____

Tree Farm

Circumference is the distance around a circle. The formula for circumference is C = πd.

Leslie's class was visiting the arboretum and one of their assignments was to measure the circumferences of certain trees. Round your answers to the nearest whole number.

A. Before the students started measuring trees, they practiced on a stump and measured the diameter first. The diameter was 14 inches. What is the circumference?

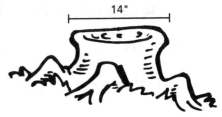

B. The students moved on to a black locust tree. This tree has a radius of 21 inches. What is the circumference?

C. The next tree was a tall and skinny loblolly pine. The students easily measured the circumference and found it was 19 inches. What is the radius?

D. The last tree was the white oak, which is the largest tree in the arboretum. The children were able to measure the circumference and it was 57 feet. Approximately what is the diameter of the tree?

Math Logic & Word Problems • 5–6 © 2005 Creative Teaching Press

Name _____ Date _____

Wagon Wheels

Mrs. Blackwell's class went to visit the local museum to see an exhibit about the wagons the pioneers used to move west. For each problem, use the information given to find both the diameter and circumference of the wagon wheels. Round your answers to the nearest whole number.

A. The stagecoach had the largest wheels. Each wheel was the same height as Glenn, who was 58 inches tall.

diameter = _____

circumference = _____

B. The Conestoga wagons had smaller wheels. The students couldn't get close enough to measure the diameter, but the museum docent had a spoke that was 19 inches long. He told the class that it was the same length as the radius of the wheel.

diameter = _____

circumference = _____

C. The buckboard, a small wagon used to go from farms or ranches to other places, was the next stop. These wheels were even smaller. A spoke measured only 14 inches.

diameter = _____

circumference = _____

D. The last wagon was the handcart that the Mormons used to bring their belongings across the plains. These carts had only two wheels and instead of being pulled by mules or oxen, they were pulled by people. The wheels on these were 36 inches tall.

diameter = _____

circumference = _____

Math Logic & Word Problems • 5–6 © 2005 Creative Teaching Press

Name _____ Date _____

Triangles

Show Me the Way

Acute Triangle—All angles measure less than 90 degrees.

Right Triangle—One angle measures 90 degrees.

Obtuse Triangle—One angle measures more than 90 degrees.

Equilateral Triangle—All angles measure the same.

All the angles in a triangle will add up to 180 degrees.

Mrs. Soto's math class has been given paper triangles, and the assignment is to classify the triangles and then to label all three angles. For each problem, there is a diagram of the triangle; name the type of triangle and label the diagram with the measurements of each angle.

A. Neal measured the first angle in his triangle and discovered it was 90 degrees. The second angle measured 60 degrees. What type of triangle is it? What is the measurement of the third angle?

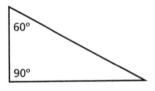

Strategic Steps

1 The clue tells us that one angle is 90 degrees. That makes it fit the description of a

_____.

2 We know that two of the angles are 90 degrees and 60 degrees. To determine the measurement of the third angle, you would add those together then subtract from 180 degrees (the total of all angles in a triangle).

180 degrees – (90 degrees + 60 degrees) = _____ degrees

B. Jerry's triangle has three equal sides and three equal angles. The one angle he measured was 60 degrees. What type of triangle is it? What are the measurements of the angles?

_____

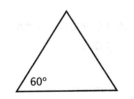

Triangles' Angles

Acute Triangle—All angles measure less than 90 degrees.

Right Triangle—One angle measures 90 degrees.

Obtuse Triangle—One angle measures more than 90 degrees.

Equilateral Triangle—All angles measure the same.

All the angles in a triangle will add up to 180 degrees.

Mrs. Soto's math class has been given paper triangles, and the assignment is to classify the triangles and then to label all three angles. For each problem, there is a diagram of the triangle; name the type of triangle and label the diagram with the measurements of each angle.

A. Todd's triangle has one very large angle of 120 degrees. The other two angles measure the same.

_____

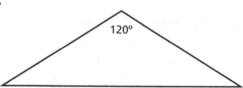

B. Carol's triangle has one angle that measures 75 degrees, a second angle that is 25 degrees less, and a third angle which is just a little larger.

_____

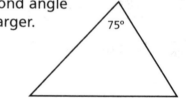

C. Heather's triangle has a right angle. The second angle is one-third of that measurement.

_____

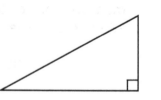

D. Ron's triangle has one angle that measures 35 degrees. Another angle is 70 degrees larger than that one.

_____

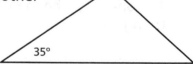

Math Logic & Word Problems • 5–6 © 2005 Creative Teaching Press

Name _____ Date _____

Assignment Triangles

> **Acute Triangle**—All angles measure less than 90 degrees.
>
> **Right Triangle**—One angle measures 90 degrees.
>
> **Obtuse Triangle**—One angle measures more than 90 degrees.
>
> **Equilateral Triangle**—All angles measure the same.
>
> All the angles in a triangle will add up to 180 degrees.

Mrs. Soto's math class has been given paper triangles, and the assignment is to classify the triangles and then to label all three angles. For each problem, there is a diagram of the triangle; name the type of triangle and label the diagram with the measurements of each angle.

A. Dylan's triangle has two angles that measure 55 degrees and 35 degrees.

_____

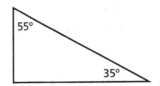

B. Kevin's triangle is tall and skinny. The top angle measures 35 degrees and the bottom two angles are equal.

_____

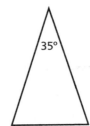

C. Kayla's triangle looks like a right triangle but when she measured the corner angle, it measured 95 degrees. The other two angles are 5 degrees apart in size.

_____

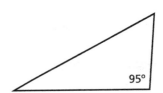

D. Rashid's triangle has equal sides and angles.

_____

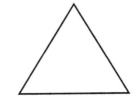

Math Logic & Word Problems • 5–6 © 2005 Creative Teaching Press

Name _____ Date _____

Area

SHOW ME THE WAY

Area of a rectangle = l × w

Area of a triangle = ½ bh

A. Dustin's rectangular bedroom is 11 feet long. When he carpeted the room, he used 143 square feet of carpeting. How wide is his bedroom?

11 ft.

x

Strategic Steps

1 We know that the formula for the area of a rectangle is length times width. We know that the bedroom is 11 feet long.

2 To find the width, you will divide the area, 143 square feet, by the length, 11 feet.

143 ÷ 11 = _____ feet (width)

B. Robin was making the backdrop for the school play. She needed to put up a triangular shaped tepee. The base will be 6 feet and the height will be 5 feet. What is the area?

Strategic Step

1 We know the formula for the area of a triangle is one-half base times height. Since the problem gives us those two numbers, it's a simple multiplication problem.

$\frac{1}{2}$ (6 feet × 5 feet) = _____ square feet

Math Logic & Word Problems • 5–6 © 2005 Creative Teaching Press

The Toy Store

Area of a rectangle = l × w   Area of a triangle = ½ bh

A. Sheri's mother owned a toy store and was moving into a larger building. The old store was 38 feet by 24 feet. The new store is 45 feet wide and has 2,385 square feet. How much larger is the new store than the old store?

B. Sheri's mother wants to use wallpaper over the office in the store. The office is a 12-foot square. The walls are 8 feet tall. How many square feet of wallpaper would be needed to cover two of the walls?

C. Sheri's mother wants to paint a large sailboat on one wall of the toy store. The sail of the boat will have a base of 8 feet and an area of 28 feet. What is the height of the sail?

D. On the front wall of the store, Sheri was going to paint large geometric shapes. She painted a circle, a square, and is now painting a triangle in bright blue. The height of the triangle is 5 feet. She wants to make the base the same as the square. The square has an area of 16 square feet. How long is the base of the triangle?

Playground

| Area of a rectangle = l × w | Area of a triangle = ½ bh |

Mr. O'Neil's class is studying area, and as a final assignment the class was going out to measure the area of playground equipment.

A. Mia and Martin were assigned to measure the area within the slide. The slide ladder is 12 feet tall. They calculated the area to be 108 square feet. How long was the area from the ladder to the bottom of the slide?

B. Jasmine and Howard found that the area inside the monkey bars was 70 feet. The monkey bars were 5 feet tall. How long were the monkey bars?

C. Charles and Miranda were measuring the area within the triangle formed by the poles holding up the swings. They found this area to be 56 square feet. The measurement between the bottoms of the poles was 7 feet. How long were the poles?

D. Aaron and Timothy were measuring the area of the swings. They found that the pole holding the swings was 21 feet and the area was 336 square feet. How tall were the swings?

Math Logic & Word Problems • 5–6 © 2005 Creative Teaching Press

Name _____ Date _____

Volume

SHOW ME THE WAY

Volume is the amount of area that fills a space. You find the volume by multiplying the length times the width times the height. Volume is expressed in cubic units.

A. Roger measured his brother's block and found it was 10 inches long and 11 inches wide. The block had a volume of 880 cubic inches. How high is the block?

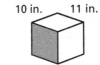

Strategic Steps

1 We know that V = lwh. The problem gives the length, width, and volume. You need to find the height.

2 Length is equal to 10 inches, width is 11 inches, and the volume is 880 cubic inches. Put those numbers into the formula.

880 cubic inches = (10 inches) × (11 inches) × (w)

880 cubic inches = _____ square inches × (w)

width = _____ inches

B. Sarah and Andrew are planting an herb garden for their mother for Mother's Day. The planter measures 40 cm long, 20 cm wide, and 30 cm tall. They bought a bag of potting soil that fills 20,000 cm³. Do they have enough potting soil?

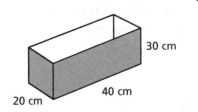

Strategic Steps

1 You have the information to find the volume of the planter, you will need to do those calculations then compare the answer to 20,000 cm³.

V = 40 cm × 20 cm × 30 cm = _____ cm³

2 Is the volume less than, more than, or equal to the amount of potting soil? _____

Math Logic & Word Problems • 5–6 © 2005 Creative Teaching Press

Name _____ Date _____

The Terrarium

Volume is the amount of area that fills a space. You find the volume by multiplying the length times the width times the height. Volume is expressed in cubic units.

Example: The box on the right has a length of 4 centimeters, a width of 2 centimeters, and is 3 centimeters high. To find the volume, use the formula V = lwh.

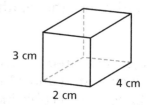

$$V = 4 \text{ cm} \times 2 \text{ cm} \times 3 \text{ cm} = 24 \text{ cm}^3$$

Lydia Rose is building a terrarium and needs to buy two sizes of gravel and soil to go in the bottom. The terrarium is 24 inches long, 14 inches wide, and 15 inches tall.

A. The bottom layer is pea gravel and needs to be 2 inches deep. How many cubic inches will she need?

B. The second layer is aquarium gravel and needs to be 1 inch deep. She has 400 cubic inches of gravel, does she have enough?

C. The top layer is potting soil. It needs to be 5 inches deep. The potting soil comes in bags of 1,500 cubic inches. How many bags will she need?

Playtime

Volume is the amount of area that fills a space. You find the volume by multiplying the length times the width times the height. Volume is expressed in cubic units.

Example: The box on the right has a length of 4 centimeters, a width of 2 centimeters, and is 3 centimeters high. To find the volume, use the formula V = lwh.

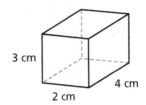

3 cm

2 cm

4 cm

$$V = 4 \text{ cm} \times 2 \text{ cm} \times 3 \text{ cm} = 24 \text{ cm}^3$$

A. Joseph was building a tower of blocks for his cousin. Each block is a 3 inch square. How many cubic inches would there be in a tower 6 blocks tall? What if the tower was 9 blocks tall?

B. Chelsea built a sandbox in the backyard for her cousins to play in. The sandbox is a square 8 feet long and 1 foot tall. How many cubic feet of sand will she need to fill the box? If the sand is sold in 50 pound bags and each bag will fill 20 cubic feet, how many bags will she need?

C. Takeshi and his dad are building a water table for his little sister. The table is 5 feet long and 1 foot deep, and holds 20 cubic feet of water. How wide is the table?

Name _____ Date _____

Time

SHOW ME THE WAY

A. Jodi was going to visit her grandmother. She left the airport at 11:13 a.m. and arrived in her grandmother's city at 4:38 p.m. How long was she in the air?

Strategic Steps

1 You need to find the elapsed time between 11:13 a.m. and 4:38 p.m. We know that from 11:13 a.m. to 12:00 p.m. (noon) is less than an hour. Subtract to find out exactly how long. Remember, there are 60 minutes in one hour.

$$60 - 13 = \text{_____} \text{ minutes}$$

2 Now, find the time from noon to 4:38 p.m.

$$12:00 \longrightarrow 4:38 = \text{_____} \text{ hours} \text{_____} \text{ minutes}$$

3 Add the times you found in steps 1 and 2 together to find the total time.

_____ + _____ = _____ hours _____ minutes (time in air)

4 Don't forget that if the minutes add up to more than 60 you should convert them into hours.

B. Amber was excited about starting her first job. She was going to be a mother's helper to a neighbor who had newborn twins. She was going to work from 9:00 a.m. to 11:30 a.m. each week day, and make $3 per hour. How much will she make each week?

Strategic Steps

1 First, find out how many hours per week Amber will work. Subtract the beginning time from the ending time.

$$9:00 \longrightarrow 11:30 = \text{_____} \text{ hours}$$

2 Now, multiply that times 5 (number of days worked) and $3 (amount earned per hour) to find out how much she will make.

_____ hours × 5 days × $3 = _____ weekly earnings

Math Logic & Word Problems • 5–6 © 2005 Creative Teaching Press

Working

A. Madigan and her classmates have volunteered to help out at the weeklong park festival. There are 12 members of the class, and together they volunteered for a total of 48 hours over 5 days. In addition, all 12 classmates will be helping at the festival for 5 hours each on Saturday. How many hours did the class volunteer during the 6 days?

B. Devin was helping his grandfather gather corn in the mornings. Each morning for 10 days he helped pick corn from 7:30 a.m. until 10:00 a.m. His grandfather paid him $100 for his work. How much did he make per hour?

C. Paloma volunteered to clean up litter along the sidewalk in front of her home for a total of 24 hours. If it took 30 minutes to walk that section of sidewalk, and she walked it daily and picked up all the litter she saw, how many days would she need to work to complete her 24 hours of volunteer time?

D. Carson wanted to ride his bike to swimming lessons every afternoon. His lesson started at 2:00 p.m. and ended at 3:15 p.m. The pool was a 15-minute bike ride from his home. If he needed to allow 10 minutes to change into his swimsuit before the lesson and 10 minutes to change out of his swimsuit after his lesson, what time does he need to leave home? What time will he return home?

Math Logic & Word Problems • 5–6 © 2005 Creative Teaching Press

Name _____   Date _____

Travel Time

A. Maggie and Satara were flying to Chicago for a band competition in another state. The plane left the airport at 11 a.m. EST and landed in Chicago at 4 p.m. CST. How long were they in the air? (Remember that there is a time change, EST is one hour ahead of CST.)

B. Patrick's family was traveling from their home to Bar Harbor, Maine for vacation. They left home at 7:12 a.m. and drove until 12:36 p.m. when they stopped for lunch. They left the fast food restaurant at 1:21 p.m. and arrived in Bar Harbor at 6:43 p.m. How long were they driving?

C. Jorge and his family had been invited to go sailing with his friend Dominic's family. They left the dock at 6:10 a.m. on Saturday morning and spent the day exploring the sea and coastline before returning to the marina at 8:43 p.m. How long were they gone?

D. Elizabeth and her family were on vacation in Nova Scotia, Canada, and visited Cape Breton National Park. There they spent one day hiking and enjoying the spectacular area. They left on their hike at 8:42 a.m. and returned at 4:36 p.m. Except for a stop from 1:03 p.m. to 1:46 p.m. to eat a picnic lunch, they walked all day. How long were they hiking?

Math Logic & Word Problems • 5–6 © 2005 Creative Teaching Press

Name _____ Date _____

Are We There Yet?

SHOW ME THE WAY

A. Jose's family is traveling from California to Chicago for vacation. If the interstate speed limit is 65 miles per hour, how far will they travel in a 12-hour day?

Strategic Steps

1 The formula for this is d = rt (d = distance; r = rate or speed; t = time).

2 Since we know the speed and time, we can fill those in the formula to find the distance.

65 mph × 12 hours = _____ miles

B. Aisha is on the school track team and can run the 400-yard dash in 65 seconds. If she runs at the same rate, how far can she run in 195 seconds?

Strategic Steps

1 The first step is to find the rate that Aisha is running.

400 = r × 65

$\frac{400}{65}$ = _____ yards per second

2 Now you have the rate; use the same formula to find the distance ran in 195 seconds.

_____ (from above) × 195 seconds = _____ yards

Math Logic & Word Problems • 5–6 © 2005 Creative Teaching Press

Traveling

A. Joseph was going with the school band to a band competition. The competition was 250 miles from Joseph's school, and they traveled for 5 hours. How fast was the school bus traveling?

B. Christian is flying from his home to his grandmother's house in a small airplane. He flew at 138 miles per hour. It took him 3 hours to get there. How far did he travel?

C. Jennifer and Garrett were hiking along the Appalachian Trail. They hiked at 2.5 miles per hour for 8 hours. How far did they travel?

D. If Jennifer and Garrett increased their rate to 3 miles per hour and traveled the same distance as in problem C, how long would it take?

Math Logic & Word Problems • 5–6 © 2005 Creative Teaching Press

Distance

A. Kendall's family is traveling on vacation. Her dad said they were 4 hours from the hotel and they were traveling at 60 miles per hour. How far will they travel?

B. The pioneers who traveled the Oregon Trail went about 2,000 miles while traveling an average of 12 miles per day. How many days did it take to travel the entire trail?

C. Forrest runs 1 mile in 6 minutes, 20 seconds. If he runs at the same rate for 22 minutes, how far will he have run? Round your answer to the nearest tenth.

D. Martina is going on a school trip with her class. They traveled at 55 miles per hour for 10 hours. How far did they travel?

Name _____ Date _____

Baking Cookies
SHOW ME THE WAY

Cookie Recipe

Ingredient	Four Dozen	Two Dozen	Twelve Dozen
butter	1 cup		
sugar	1½ cups		
eggs	2		
flour	3 cups		
walnuts	1 cup		
chocolate chips	1 cup		

A. Mrs. Gray Eagle was baking cookies for the school bake sale. Her recipe made four dozen cookies, but she needs to make two dozen cookies. How much of each ingredient will she need?

Strategic Step

① To go from four dozen to two dozen cookies, you will need to divide by 2. Instead of 1 cup of butter, you would reduce the amount to ½ cup. Fill in the "Two Dozen" column on the chart.

B. Mrs. Dawes used the same recipe to make cookies to have as refreshments after the band concert. She needs twelve dozen cookies. How much of each ingredient does she need?

Strategic Step

① To go from four dozen to twelve dozen, what number will you need to multiply by? Multiply all ingredients by that number. Fill in the "Twelve Dozen" column on the chart.

Math Logic & Word Problems • 5–6 © 2005 Creative Teaching Press

Birthday Party

A. Mrs. Sandy's class is planning a surprise birthday party for her. Debbie and Marcus are in charge of making the lemonade. How much of each ingredient do they need to make enough 1-cup servings for 50 people?

Lemonade

Ingredient	6 Cups	50 Cups
lemons	3	
water	6 cups	
sugar	⅔ cup	

B. Helen and Glenn are going to bake the brownies for the party. How much of each ingredient do they need to make 60 brownies?

Brownies

Ingredient	One Dozen	Five Dozen
unsweetened cocoa powder	⅓ cup	
flour	1 cup	
baking powder	1 teaspoon	
salt	½ teaspoon	
butter	½ cup	
eggs	2	
sugar	1⅔ cups	

Math Logic & Word Problems • 5–6 © 2005 Creative Teaching Press

Name _____   Date _____

Pizza Fun

Bontu, Khaliq, Joy, and Gwyn were going to have a pizza party for their school. They have recipes for dough and sauce from the pizza parlor that Khaliq's father owns. They want to make 75 pizzas.

Use the tables to find the amount of each ingredient needed to make 75 pizzas.

Pizza Dough

Ingredient	10 Pizzas	75 Pizzas
warm water	9 cups	
active yeast	10 tablespoons	
sugar	10 teaspoons	
salt	5 teaspoons	
oil	20 tablespoons	
flour	6 cups	

Pizza Sauce

Ingredient	25 Pizzas	75 Pizzas
tomatoes	12, medium-sized	
onions	3 bulbs	
sugar	4 teaspoons	
fresh basil	10 teaspoons	
garlic	5 cloves	

Math Logic & Word Problems • 5–6 © 2005 Creative Teaching Press

How Much Do I Need?

SHOW ME THE WAY

A. You are making tuna casserole for dinner and need 2 cups of egg noodles. When you go to the store, all the packages are in ounces, not cups. From your cooking class at school, you remember that 2 ounces is ½ cup. Do you need to buy the 4-ounce, 6-ounce, or 12-ounce bag of egg noodles?

Strategic Steps

For this you must convert from a weight measurement to a volume measurement.

1 The problem tells you that 2 ounces of egg noodles equals ½ cup. Now you need to find how many ½ cups are in 2 cups.

2 Since there are two ½ cup measures in 1 cup, you would multiply 2 × 2 = 4.

3 Now, multiply that number by 2 ounces. 4 × 2 = _____ ounces

4 Which of the bags will have enough egg noodles for your recipe? _____

B. You are making the same tuna casserole for a family reunion. The original recipe is for 4 servings but you need to make 16 servings. How many 6-ounce bags of egg noodles will you need?

_____

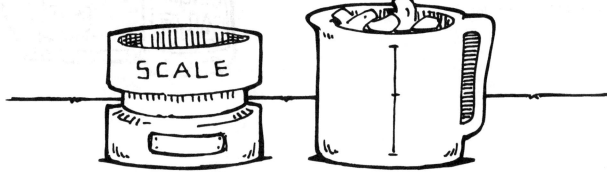

Now You Are Cooking

A. Scott and Tanner are making macaroni and cheese for their camp group. There are 20 kids in the group. To make 20 servings of macaroni and cheese, Scott and Tanner need 10 cups of elbow macaroni. One cup of elbow macaroni weighs 6 ounces. How many ounces will give them enough macaroni to make their recipe? The store has two 8-ounce bags of macaroni and the rest are packaged in 4-ounce bags. How many of each size will they need?

B. Rashid was making vegetable soup for his family. The recipe called for 800 milliliters of tomato juice. He had several cans of tomato juice, but the weight was in grams. He opened one can of tomato juice that weighed 150 grams and it measured 100 milliliters. The other cans he had were two each of 800 grams, 150 grams, and 400 grams. Which of the cans did he need to make his soup?

C. Miranda is making punch. The recipe is in quarts, but the ingredients are only sold in liters. A 2-liter bottle of ginger ale is equal to 2 quarts, 3.6 ounces. She needs 9 quarts of ginger ale for the punch. How many 2-liter bottles does she need? (There are 32 ounces in a quart.)

Math Logic & Word Problems • 5–6 © 2005 Creative Teaching Press

Name _____   Date _____

In the Kitchen

A. Albert is learning how to make bean soup. The recipe calls for ¼ cup each of 16 types of beans. If 1 cup of beans weighs 5 ounces, how many ounces of beans does Albert need?

B. Cassi is making punch. The recipe is in quarts, but the ingredients are only sold in liters. The recipe calls for 7 quarts of ginger ale. Cassi knows that 1 ounce equals 29.57 milliliters. How many liters of ginger ale does she need?

Math Logic & Word Problems • 5–6 © 2005 Creative Teaching Press

The Sleepover

Show Me the Way

A. Emily, Emma, Aisha, and Paige are shopping for a sleepover they are having this weekend. They want to buy pizza toppings to make pizzas.

The pepperoni costs $3.20 per pound, and they want to buy 6 ounces. How much will it cost?

Strategic Steps

1 First, you need to find out how much the pepperoni costs per ounce. There are 16 ounces in a pound so you would divide the cost by 16 ounces.

$3.20 ÷ 16 = _____ per ounce

2 Now, multiply that number times the 6 ounces they want to buy.

_____ per ounce × 6 ounces = _____ cost

B. They could buy whole mushrooms for $2.50 for a half pound, or pay $2.75 for a 4-ounce box of sliced mushrooms. Which one is less expensive?

Strategic Steps

1 First find out how much each type of mushroom will cost per pound. How many ounces are in a half pound?

Sliced $2.75 ÷ 4 = _____ cost per ounce

Whole $2.50 ÷ _____ ounces = _____ cost per ounce

2 Compare the costs per ounce. Which is less expensive? _____

Math Logic & Word Problems • 5–6 © 2005 Creative Teaching Press

The Fruit Stand

A. One pear weighs 85 grams. How many pears would be in a bag weighing 1 kilogram? (Round to the nearest whole number.) If 1 kilogram costs $5, how much would one pear cost?

B. A bushel of apples weighs 27.5 pounds and there are 55 apples in the bushel. Approximately how many ounces does an apple weigh?

C. Yonni wants to make blueberry cobbler and needs 3 cups of blueberries. All the blueberries are packaged in 0.5 kilogram containers. The fruit stand attendant told Yonni that 1 cup of blueberries weighs about 250 grams. How many packages of blueberries will Yonni need?

D. Ashley wants to buy kiwis for a fruit salad. Each kiwi weighs approximately 2.5 ounces. Kiwis cost $5.50 per pound. If she buys 12 kiwis, how much will they cost?

Math Logic & Word Problems • 5–6 © 2005 Creative Teaching Press

Dinner Plans

Lucy was making dinner for her friends. She has a recipe for beef and broccoli and wants to buy all the ingredients. There are 5 members of Lucy's family, plus 4 friends, to make a total of 9 people at dinner.

A. She wants to use top round beef and it costs $3.59 per pound. She'll need 3 ounces per person. How much will the beef cost?

B. The broccoli costs $1.29 a bunch. Each bunch weighs approximately 1 pound and she needs 5 ounces per person. How many bunches will she need? Will she use it all? (Round to the nearest whole number.)

C. She needs to use ¼ cup uncooked rice per person. How much rice will she need?

D. For dessert, she wants to buy a fruit salad. The recommended serving is 6 ounces per person, and it is sold in either ½ pound or 1 pound containers. How much will she need?

Math Logic & Word Problems • 5–6 © 2005 Creative Teaching Press

Name _____   Date _____

  # Candy Store
SHOW ME THE WAY

Kira, Ian, and Gwyn stopped at the candy store after school.

- Kira spent $3.35 on candy; Ian spent 35 cents less than Kira; and Gwyn spent half as much as Ian.
- Ian bought 2 peanut butter balls and the same number of fudge squares. He spent as much on chocolate caramels as on cherry rolls.
- Kira bought 1 fewer chocolate caramel than Ian, and twice as many fudge squares as Ian. She spent the rest of her money on lemon drops.
- Gwyn bought 3 more peanut butter balls than Ian, and also decided to try the chocolate caramels and cherry rolls.

Candy	Cost
Peanut butter ball	15 cents
Lemon drop	20 cents
Chocolate caramel	25 cents
Fudge square	35 cents
Cherry roll	50 cents

Strategic Steps

1 Make a table to show how much each child spent and on which candy. First, fill it in with the direct information you found.

Name	Amount	Caramels	Balls	Drops	Squares	Rolls
Kira	$3.35	3			4	
Ian			2		2	
Gwen			5			

2 Determine how much each child spent. Then use the clues to fill out the remaining squares in your chart.

3 Check your work by adding together the cost of the candy for each child.

Park Lunch

Coley, Decker, Julie, Ryan, Anika, and Kali met for lunch at the park patio stand. The waiter took their orders but then forgot who got which lunch. Using the following clues match each of the six orders to the correct child.

- Coley paid with three $1 bills. She got 3 quarters and 1 nickel back in change.

- Decker paid with a $5 bill and received three $1 bills and 3 dimes in change.

- Julie paid with a $1 bill, three quarters, and one dime.

- Ryan paid with two $1 bills and one quarter, and received 2 dimes in change.

- Anika paid with two $1 bills and received a nickel back in change.

- Kali paid with 7 quarters and received 2 dimes in change.

Item	Cost
Taco	65 cents
Hot dog	75 cents
Hamburger	95 cents
Chips	40 cents
Fries	70 cents
Apple juice	55 cents
Milk	50 cents
Ice cream	90 cents

Order 1

Taco

Milk

Ice cream

_____

Order 2

Hot dog

Chips

Apple juice

_____

Order 3

Hamburger

Fries

Apple juice

_____

Order 4

Taco

Chips

Milk

_____

Order 5

Hot dog

Fries

Milk

_____

Order 6

Hamburger

Chips

Milk

_____

Math Logic & Word Problems • 5–6 © 2005 Creative Teaching Press

School Supplies

Mrs. Kittleson offered to take all six of her grandchildren shopping for school supplies. Each of the kids had a different list. Once they all picked out their supplies, Mrs. Kittleson gave them each a $5 bill to pay for the supplies. She mixed up the lists and didn't remember which one went to which grandchild; use the following clues to match the child with the correct list.

- Kris needed two glue sticks. He received 3 quarters and 3 pennies in change.

- Alyssa needed one of everything. She received a $1 bill plus 2 quarters, 1 penny, 1 nickel and 1 dime in change.

- Brodie needed at least one of everything except an eraser. He needed the same number of pencils as Maria. He got $0.47 in change from his $5 bill.

- Jared needed twice as many crayons as Alyssa. He got two $1 bills and 1 penny back in change.

- Maria only needed four different items, but needed five times as many folders as Brodie. Maria spent ½ of her $5 bill.

- Betsy needed twice as many folders as Brodie. She got back $2.74 in change.

Item	Cost
Crayons	34 cents
Notebook	12 cents
Paper	50 cents
Binder	99 cents
Folder	7 cents
Pencils	48 cents
Eraser	15 cents
Glue stick	69 cents

List 1
1 glue stick
1 paper
5 folders
2 pencils

List 2
2 crayons
1 glue stick
1 binder
1 pencil
1 eraser

List 3
1 paper
1 binder
2 folders
1 pencil
1 eraser

List 4
2 glue sticks   1 eraser
2 notebooks
1 paper
1 binder
2 pencils

List 5
1 crayon   1 folder
1 glue stick   1 pencil
1 notebook   1 eraser
1 paper
1 binder

List 6
1 crayon   1 folder
1 glue stick   2 pencils
4 notebooks
2 papers
1 binder

Ratio and Probability

SHOW ME THE WAY

A **ratio** is a comparison of two quantities. **Probability** is the ratio of favorable outcomes to possible outcomes.

A. Write the ratio of these items in three ways.

Strategic Steps

1 Ratios can be written as fractions, or as a number comparing the objects as in 1:2, or using words, 1 to 2.

2 In this case, we have 2 birds and 3 trees. Write this as a fraction. _____

3 Write the same ratio using the 1:2 format. _____ : _____

4 Write the same ratio using the 1 to 2 format. _____ to _____

B. Alice writes down the names of each child in her class and puts them in a box. There are 9 girls and 14 boys. What is the probability of each person's name being chosen?

Strategic Steps

1 Remember, probability is the number of favorable outcomes compared to the number of possible outcomes. In this case, the possible outcomes include all the students in the class. Add together the number of girls and boys to find the number of total students.

$$9 + 14 = _____$$

2 If Alice is drawing one name, then the number of favorable outcomes is just 1. That means the probability is going to be 1/ _____ (total students).

Math Logic & Word Problems • 5–6 © 2005 Creative Teaching Press

Name _____ Date _____

Ratios

A **ratio** is a comparison of two quantities. **Probability** is the ratio of favorable outcomes to possible outcomes.

A. Write the ratio of cars to motorcycles in three ways.

_____   _____ : _____   _____ to _____

B. Write the ratio of suns to moons in three ways.

_____   _____ : _____   _____ to _____

C. Frank reaches into a bag that contains 8 striped marbles, 12 polka-dotted marbles, and 7 solid marbles. What is the probability he will pick a striped marble?

_____

D. Lisa has a bag with 24 green beads and 48 red beads. What is the probability that she will choose a green bead? Reduce that to lowest terms.

_____

Name _____ Date _____

Comparing

A **ratio** is a comparison of two quantities. **Probability** is the ratio of favorable outcomes to possible outcomes.

A. There are 28 girls and 35 boys in the fifth grade at Lakeside Elementary. Write the ratio of girls to boys in three ways.

_____   _____:_____   _____ to _____

B. Barney went on an animal watching trip. He saw 12 mammals and 14 birds. Write the ratio of mammals to birds in three different ways. Reduce your answers to the lowest terms.

_____   _____:_____   _____ to _____

C. A regular deck of playing cards has 52 cards—4 suits with 13 cards in each. If you draw only one card, what is the probability that you will draw a 4?

_____

In the same deck of cards, what is the probability of drawing a heart?

_____

D. Ashley collected names of the students who are interested in joining the band. There were 6 boys and 9 girls who wanted to play drums. Ashley put all the names into a box to draw to see who will be able to learn to play drums. What is the probability of each name being drawn?

_____

What would the probability be if three names were drawn?

_____

Math Logic & Word Problems • 5–6 © 2005 Creative Teaching Press

Percentages

SHOW ME THE WAY

A. Roman makes $50 per week and spends 40% of his income on entertainment. How much does he spend?

Strategic Steps

1 First, convert the percentage to a decimal. This is done by dropping the percentage sign and moving the decimal point two places to the left.

$$40\% = 0.40$$

2 Multiply the decimal by the amount.

$$\$50 \times 0.40 = _____ \text{ amount spent on entertainment}$$

B. North Middle School has an enrollment of 3,500 students in sixth through eighth grade. Seventy-five percent of these students are seventh and eighth grade students. How many students are in the sixth grade?

Strategic Steps

1 First, convert the percentage to a decimal.

$$75\% \text{ equals } 0.75$$

2 Multiply the decimal by the number.

$$3,500 \times 0.75 = _____ \text{ number of other students}$$

3 Subtract the number of seventh and eighth grade students from the total students.

$$3,500 - _____ \text{ (number of other students)} = _____ \text{ number of sixth grade students}$$

Percents Are Fun

A. Patrick has 350 baseball cards. Thirty-five percent of them are gifts from his parents. How many cards have his parents bought for him? (Round to the nearest whole number.)

B. Jimmy is helping plan the class' week-long camping trip. The trip will cost a total of $1,500. Exactly 60% will be used for the camp fees and other supplies; the remaining amount will be used for food. How much will the food cost?

C. Cyrus collects stamps. He has 478 stamps in his collection. Twenty-five percent of the stamps are from countries other than the United States. How many United States stamps does he have? (Round to the nearest whole number.)

D. Rose plays clarinet in the school band. There are 76 students in the band and 20% play woodwind instruments. How many students play non-woodwind instruments? (Round to the nearest whole number.)

Math Logic & Word Problems • 5–6 © 2005 Creative Teaching Press

Name _____ Date _____

What Percent Is Left?

A. The O'Neil family has budgeted $75 per month on entertainment costs. They spend 30% of that on video rental. How much do they spend each month to rent videos?

B. Gretchyn helped her scout troop collect newspapers to pay for a trip. They collected 2,350 pounds of newspapers. Twenty percent of the papers came from the scouts' families. How many pounds of newspapers did other community members donate?

C. Meagan has 612 students in her grade level. Forty-six percent of the students are in the band, orchestra, or chorus. How many students are not in a musical program? (Round to the nearest whole number.)

D. Edmundo has 750 tulip bulbs. Twenty-eight percent of the tulips are red in color. How many tulips are not red?

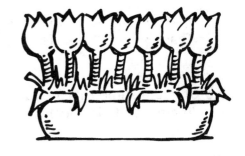

Math Logic & Word Problems • 5–6 © 2005 Creative Teaching Press

Name _____ Date _____

Baseball Tournament

SHOW ME THE WAY

There are eight baseball teams playing in a tournament.

- In the first round of the tournament, each team will play all the other teams. The four teams who win the most games will play in the second round.
- In the second round, each team will play one game. The winners of these games will play in the final round.
- The winner of the final round will win the tournament.

How many games will the winning team have played? _____

Strategic Steps

1 You need to draw a chart to find the answer. Name the teams Team 1, Team 2, and so on to label the chart.

Round One:

Team 1 ———— Team 2
———— Team 3
———— Team 4
———— Team 5
———— Team 6
———— Team 7
———— Team 8

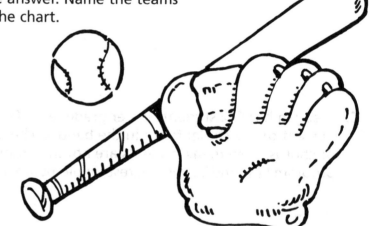

2 If you assume that Teams 1 through 4 won the most games, then the order of play in the second round is as follows:

Team 1　　　　Team 2
Team 3　　　　Team 4

3 If you assume that Team 1 and Team 4 won their games, then in the third round Team 1 will play against Team 4.

4 To find the answer, count the number of games that Team 1 played.

Math Logic & Word Problems • 5–6 © 2005 Creative Teaching Press

Tennis Match

Ten players enter a tennis tournament. There will be three rounds.

- In the first round, each player will play all other players. The four players who win the most matches will play in the second round.

- In the second round, each player will only play one match against one of the other players.

- In the third and final round, the two winners from the second round will play each other. The winner of this match is the winner of the tournament.

How many tennis matches will the winner of the tournament have played? _____

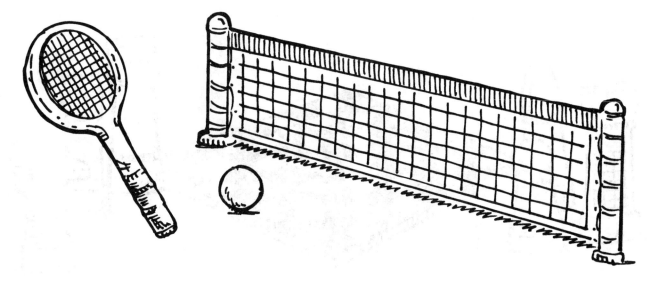

Name _____ Date _____

All City Chess

Caroline entered the All City Chess tournament. There were a total of twelve players.

- For the first round, all twelve players played each of the other players. The six players who win the most games will play in the second round.

- In the second round, all six players will play each of the other players. The four players who win the most games will play in the semifinals.

- In the semifinals, each of the four players will play one game, the winner of these two games, will play in the finals.

- Caroline played in the finals and won the game and tournament.

How many total games of chess did she play? _____

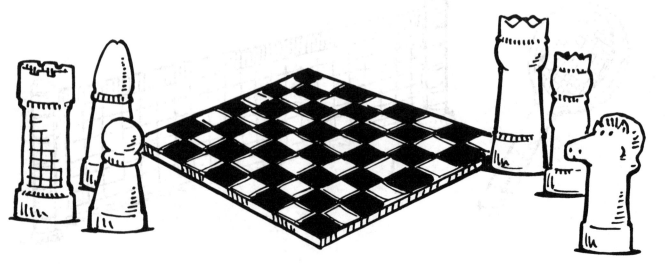

Math Logic & Word Problems • 5–6 © 2005 Creative Teaching Press

Name _____ Date _____

Ice-Cream Sundae

SHOW ME THE WAY

Your favorite ice-cream flavors are vanilla, chocolate, strawberry, butter pecan, rocky road, and peanut butter cup. You can make a sundae using two of these flavors. How many different combinations can you make?

Strategic Steps

1 List the possible combinations in order to count them. Remember that vanilla and chocolate are the same as chocolate and vanilla and should not be repeated.

Vanilla ——————— Chocolate
——— Strawberry
——— Butter Pecan
——— Rocky Road
——— Peanut Butter Cup

Chocolate ——————— Strawberry
——— Butter Pecan
——— Rocky Road
——— Peanut Butter Cup

Strawberry ——————— Butter Pecan
——— Rocky Road
——— Peanut Butter Cup

Butter Pecan ——————— Rocky Road
——— Peanut Butter Cup

Rocky Road ——————— Peanut Butter Cup

Peanut Butter Cup ——— no new mixtures

2 Once you have your list, go back and count the flavor pairs.

How many different combinations of flavors did you count? _____

Math Logic & Word Problems • 5–6 © 2005 Creative Teaching Press

Your Order, Please

Your family is going to try the new restaurant in town. They have an omelet bar and everyone will be able to order an omelet with their favorite fillings. The filling choices for omelets are: cheese, mushrooms, peppers, ham, bacon, broccoli, onions, and tomato.

Cheese ⎯⎯⎯⎯⎯

Ham ⎯⎯⎯⎯⎯

Bacon ⎯⎯⎯⎯⎯

Mushrooms ⎯⎯⎯⎯⎯

Broccoli ⎯⎯⎯⎯⎯

Onions ⎯⎯⎯⎯⎯

Peppers ⎯⎯⎯⎯⎯

Tomato ⎯⎯⎯⎯⎯

How many different combinations did you find? _____

Math Logic & Word Problems • 5–6 © 2005 Creative Teaching Press

Name _____ Date _____

School Colors

Your school is having a Bright Color Day and each day you will wear two arm bands in two of the following colors: red, blue, yellow, green, black, white, orange, brown, pink, and purple. You and your classmates are trying to find out how many combinations there are.

Red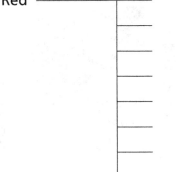

Green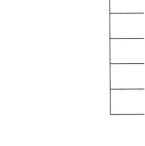

Black

White

Orange

Brown

Blue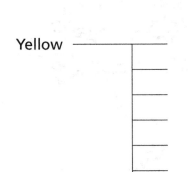

Pink ————————————

Yellow

Purple ————————————

How many possible color combinations are there? _____

Camp Activities

Show Me the Way

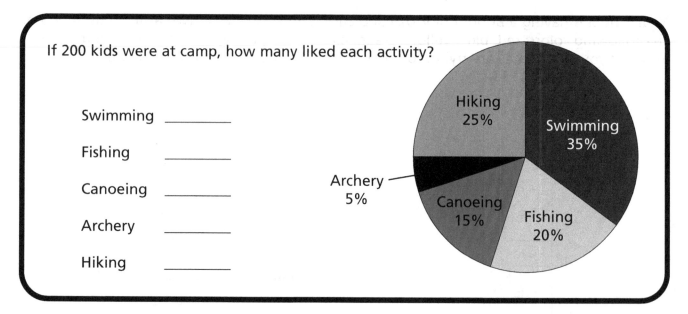

If 200 kids were at camp, how many liked each activity?

Swimming _____

Fishing _____

Canoeing _____

Archery _____

Hiking _____

Hiking 25%

Swimming 35%

Archery 5%

Canoeing 15%

Fishing 20%

Strategic Step

To find the number of campers who like each of the activities you will multiply the total number of campers by the percent that likes that activity. For example, 5% like archery, so you would multiply .05 × 200 campers.

Math Logic & Word Problems • 5–6 © 2005 Creative Teaching Press

Zoo Animals

As part of a school report, Ashley found the local zoo had 450 animals and classified them by groups.

How many animals are in each group?

Mammals _____

Birds _____

Reptiles _____

Amphibians _____

Insects _____

Fish _____

Other _____

Reptiles 10%

Birds 12%

Mammals 35%

Fish 8%

Amphibians 5%

Insects 25%

Other 5%

Favorite Subject

Abigail did a survey of the 30 students in Mr. Morris' class to find out their favorite subjects.

How many students like each subject?

Spelling _____

Reading _____

Math _____

Science _____

History _____

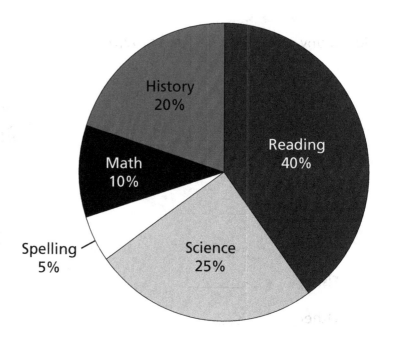

Math Logic & Word Problems • 5–6 © 2005 Creative Teaching Press

Favorite Colors

SHOW ME THE WAY

Ashley, Olivia, Ngan, and Latasha are friends whose favorite colors are red, blue, green, and pink. Use the following clues to match each girl with her favorite color.

- Olivia's favorite color does not have an "e" in it.
- Ngan often compliments Ashley on her green sweater.
- Ngan's favorite color does not have an "r" in it.
- Ashley never wears her favorite color.

	Red	Blue	Green	Pink
Ashley				
Olivia				
Ngan				
Latasha				

Strategic Steps

1 Working with the first clue, it's easy to eliminate all the colors that have an "e". Next to Olivia's name, lightly put an "X" in each box of a color that can be eliminated. This will leave one color, pink. Write a large "Y" for yes, in the pink box.

2 In the rows for the other girls, lightly put an "X" in the column under pink. Because that color has been assigned, the other girls cannot have that as a favorite color.

3 The second clue doesn't really help match either girl with a favorite color, so move on to the next clue. The third clue says that Ngan's favorite color does not have an "r" in it. Mark out the colors with an "r", and that leaves blue as Ngan's favorite color. Eliminate blue as a possibility for the other girls.

4 The fourth clue says that Ashley never wears her favorite color, going back to the second clue where we learned that Ashley often wears a green sweater. Use those two clues to find Ashley's and Latasha's favorite colors.

Math Logic & Word Problems • 5–6 © 2005 Creative Teaching Press

Name _____ Date _____

Ice Cream

Soren, Silas, Ruthann, Victoria, and Julia went out for ice cream. Each ordered an ice-cream cone in their favorite flavor. Use the following clues to match each child with his or her favorite flavor.

- Only one child orders ice cream that starts with the same first letter as their name.

- Julia's favorite ice cream is the same color as her favorite color.

- The name of the child who orders strawberry ice cream does not start with "S".

- Silas orders ice cream with more than one flavor.

- Soren does not like peppermint.

- Ruthann does not like fruit flavored ice cream.

	Strawberry	Vanilla	Chocolate	Mint Chocolate Chip	Peppermint
Soren					
Silas					
Ruthann					
Victoria					
Julia					

Math Logic & Word Problems • 5–6 © 2005 Creative Teaching Press

Birthdays

Mitchell, Kendall, Olivia, Madeline, and Cody are talking about their birthdays. None were born in the same month. Use the following clues to match each child with their birth month.

- None of the children were born in the month that starts with the letter starting their names.

- Kendall's birthday falls on a holiday where people dress up.

- Madeline usually plants a new flowering plant in the warm days around her birthday.

- Last year, Cody's birthday was on the last day of school.

- Olivia's birthday is on the first day of spring.

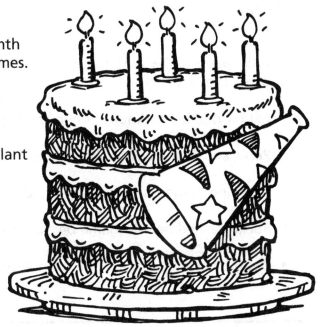

	January	March	April	May	October
Michell					
Kendall					
Olivia					
Madeline					
Cody					

Math Logic & Word Problems • 5–6 © 2005 Creative Teaching Press

Nicknames

Julie, Pat, Ty, Peter, and Debbie have been given the nicknames Sunshine, Twinkle Toes, Bubbles, Rocky, and Slugger. Use the following clues to match each child with his or her nickname.

- Julie was with Twinkle Toes who earned the nickname when he fell into a creek they were crossing.

- Pat earned her nickname when she kept striking out.

- Peter and Twinkle Toes like to hike together on weekends.

- Sunshine earned his nickname for the sunny smile he gave his mother as an infant.

- Rocky earned her nickname because her hobby is collecting rocks.

- Debbie has a necklace made from a quartz crystal she found.

	Sunshine	Twinkle Toes	Bubbles	Rocky	Slugger
Julie					
Pat					
Ty					
Peter					
Debbie					

Math Logic & Word Problems • 5–6 © 2005 Creative Teaching Press

Bird Watching

Dena, Wendy, Steven, Carl, and Cindy are members of the nature club. On the recent bird watching field trip, they each decided that one of the following birds is their favorite. The birds they like are American robin, cardinal, Canada goose, golden eagle, and blue jay. Use the following clues to match each student with their favorite bird.

- No child's first name starts with the same letter as his or her favorite bird.

- Wendy's favorite bird is a relative of our national symbol.

- Steven's favorite bird migrates to a country north of us to nest each year.

- Carl's favorite color is blue and so is his favorite bird.

	American Robin	Cardinal	Canada Goose	Golden Eagle	Blue Jay
Dena					
Wendy					
Steven					
Carl					
Cindy					

Toy Time

Mrs. Regan's class was studying personal history in social studies, and this week's assignment was to bring in a toy that was their favorite before they started kindergarten. Jayson, Emily, Tom, Marta, and Logan brought in blocks, cars, a baby doll, an action figure, and a plush bear. Use the following clues to match each student with their favorite toy.

- Tom and Marta used to play with the owner of the action figure at her house.

- Jayson has moved up to making models of his favorite toy.

- Logan's favorite toy can be stacked together.

- Marta's favorite toy is similar to an animal.

	Blocks	Cars	Baby Doll	Action Figure	Plush Bear
Jayson					
Emily					
Tom					
Marta					
Logan					

Math Logic & Word Problems • 5–6 © 2005 Creative Teaching Press

Lunchtime

Alice, Scott, Linda, Curtis, and Joyce were eating lunch at the mall. Each ordered a different meal. The meals include: Chinese steamed vegetables, cheeseburger, pepperoni pizza, Chef's salad (includes cheese cubes and ham), and chicken nuggets. Match each child with his or her lunch.

- Alice does not eat cheese.

- Scott likes bread with his meal, but does not like tomato sauce.

- Joyce does not eat meat.

- Linda's lunch is flat with slices of round meat.

	Chinese Steamed Vegetables	Cheeseburger	Pepperoni Pizza	Chef's Salad	Chicken Nuggets
Alice					
Scott					
Linda					
Curtis					
Joyce					

Answer Key

Place Value (page 5)

A. 469.456

What Place? (page 6)

A. 5853.461

B. 356.845

C. 9255.224

D. 1515.315

Number Arrangement (page 7)

A. 828.474

B. 3192.571

C. 2079.441

D. 5640.876

Decimals (page 8)

A. 0.23

B. Madison—0.45 miles

Wesley—0.64 miles

Lara—1.9 miles

Aaron—2.01 miles

Kathy—3.7 miles

More Decimals (page 9)

A. 0.42

B. 2.27 packs

C. 5.2 bottles

D. 1.07 acres

1.3 acres

1.705 acres

1.74 acres

1.75 acres

Cameron's Day (page 10)

A. 0.71

B. 0.275

C. Deer—1.34 g

Beaver—1.2 g

Buffalo—0.98 g

Alligator—0.83 g

Fox—0.75 g

D. 7.15 feet of track

Peanut Hunt (page 11)

No, they only found 96 peanuts. There are still 4 to be found.

Can Drive (page 12)

Yes, they collected 793 cans.

Gold Rush (page 13)

They need to continue. They have only found 48 pounds, 14 ounces.

The Wedding (page 14)

A. 24

B. 19

National Parks (page 15)

A. 983 miles

B. 3.5 kilometers

C. 32 elk

D. $4.33 on postcards

The Aquarium (page 16)

A. 5 bags

B. 5 in display, 7 in each aquarium

C. 4 in display, 4 in each aquarium

D. 4 tetras in the tank

E. 8 tetras

Guess How Many (page 17)

A. 5 letters and 3 postcards

B. 3 people and 4 ants, 6 people and 3 ants, or 9 people and 2 ants

Summer Trips (page 18)

A. 8 apples, 4 oranges

B. 12 horses, 12 people

C. 6 tents

D. 6 cars, 3 motorcycles

Ready for School (page 19)

A. 24 pencils, 6 erasers
B. 18 dogs, 22 people
C. 16 chocolate, 34 white milk
D. 32 chairs, 12 people

Implied Steps (page 20)

A. 48 miles driven per day
   240 miles driven per week
   960 miles driven per month

B. Hours worked each week: 50 hours
   Amount made per week: $250.00
   Amount made per month: $1,000
   Amount made over 2-month time: $2,000

Summer Vacation (page 21)

A. Amount made per day: $60
   Amount made in July: $1,860

B. Amount of water per day: 10 gallons
   Water carried during August: 310 gallons

C. Distance per day: 4 miles
   Distance in July: 124 miles

Music Lessons (page 22)

A. Hours practiced per day: 2 hours
   Hours practiced per week: 14 hours
   Hours practiced per month: 56 hours

B. Cost of lessons per week: $24
   Cost of lessons per month: $96
   Cost of lessons for 6 months: $576

C. Hours practiced in a year: 365 hours
   Hours taking lessons per week: 2 hours
   Hours taking lessons per month: 8 hours
   Hours taking lessons per year: 96 hours
   Hours playing the piano during the year: 461 hours

Fraction Puzzles (page 23)

A. $\frac{3}{8} + \frac{4}{8} = \frac{7}{8}$
B. $\frac{8}{15} - \frac{7}{15} = \frac{1}{15}$

Fraction Sums and Differences (page 24)

A. $\frac{2}{3} + \frac{2}{3} = \frac{4}{3} = 1\frac{1}{3}$
B. $\frac{9}{12} - \frac{3}{12} = \frac{6}{12} = \frac{1}{2}$
C. $\frac{13}{21} + \frac{17}{21} = \frac{30}{21} = 1\frac{3}{7}$
D. $\frac{8}{9} - \frac{2}{9} = \frac{6}{9} = \frac{2}{3}$

Fraction Addition and Subtraction (page 25)

A. $\frac{1}{2} + \frac{3}{6} = 1$
B. $\frac{8}{6} + \frac{10}{12} = \frac{18}{12} = 1\frac{1}{2}$
C. $\frac{8}{12} - \frac{2}{6} = \frac{1}{3}$
D. $\frac{20}{24} - \frac{3}{6} = \frac{8}{24} = \frac{1}{3}$

Can You Guess? (page 26)

A. 4 pennies, 3 dimes, 5 nickels, and 3 quarters
B. The numbers are 12 and 14.

Your Guess, Please (page 27)

A. Bison—8; Cranes—13
B. The blouse, sweater, and T-shirt
C. The numbers are 3 and 39.
D. Corn and watermelon

Can You Double-Check That? (page 28)

A. Dogs—4; Birds—10
B. 1 quarter; 2 nickels; 8 pennies
C. The numbers are 13 and 12.
D. Forest has 12 cards and Emil has 8 cards.

The Game (page 29)

A. 78
B. 3.8 kilometers

Veterinarian Clinic (page 30)

A. 8.94 pounds
B. 354.08 dogs
C. $9.00

Jobs (page 31)

A. 76 minutes
B. 15.75 dozen
C. $20
D. 76 pounds

Checkbook Math (page 32)

$30.00 to cover the negative balance. Checkbook balance should be $2.80.

Yard Work (page 33)

Balance—$11.09

Mistakes (page 34)

Balance as of June 20			23.76
Deposit June 21		+25.00	48.76
Music Store	−22.98		25.78
Toy Store	−14.23		11.55
Deposit		+16.00	27.55
Department Store	−32.14		−4.59
Bank fee	−20.00	−24.59	
Deposit July 8		+25.00	0.41

Sean made a mistake when he subtracted the Toy Store debit. He also added the $16.00 deposit incorrectly.

First Jobs (page 35)

A. 5 months
B. $5

Earning and Spending (page 36)

A. 3 months
B. $1.50
C. $90

How Long? (page 37)

A. 18 weeks
B. $4.00
C. 4 weeks

Jelly Beans (page 38)

87 jelly beans

The Penny Jar (page 39)

95 pennies

Marbles (page 40)

162 marbles

Let's Double (page 41)

Mrs. Bartee would have 1,024 bromeliads after ten years.

Science Experiment (page 42)

10 generations would produce 2,560 amoebae.

Charlotte's Decision (page 43)

Day 14 would be $81.92. Charlotte should choose to receive a penny doubled every day for 14 days.

Reading Contest (page 44)

Pete—24 pages
Chalondra—42 pages
Betty—12 pages
Margaret—18 pages

Basketball Game (page 45)

Jethro—70 points
Peter—12 points
Jack—6 points
Max—14 points
Forrest—10 points

Tulips (page 46)

Friday—12 bulbs
Saturday—36 bulbs
Sunday—50 bulbs
Monday—30 bulbs
Tuesday—30 bulbs
Wednesday—30 bulbs
Thursday—30 bulbs
Friday—46 bulbs
Saturday—36 bulbs

Venn Diagram (page 47)

Three students take only gymnastics.

Gymnastics Challenges (page 48)

A. 10 students
B. 16 students

More Diagrams (page 49)

A. 39 students
B. 35 students

Who Is First? (page 50)

Matthew, Hannah, Emma, Mike, Rachel

Which Floor? (page 51)

Nadia—fifth floor
Carol—third floor
Mario—second floor
Kai—first floor
Bailey—fourth floor

Band Concert (page 52)

Zane, Dominic, Cassandra, Danny, Joey, Meagan

Magic Squares (page 53)

4	9	2
3	5	7
8	1	6

Could It Be Magic? (page 54)

10	5	6
3	7	11
8	9	4

16	3	2	13
5	10	11	8
9	6	7	12
4	15	14	1

Math Magic (page 55)

1	8	11	14
12	13	2	7
6	3	16	9
15	10	5	4

33	15	23	9
27	5	29	19
13	35	11	21
7	25	17	31

Prizes (page 56)

A. 250 books
50 games
25 movies
B. 50
C. 25

Lockers (page 57)

A. pencil—128
eraser—76
notebook—7
B. 25
C. 2

All Aboard! (page 58)

A. 32
B. 9
C. Yes. One person will receive both a postcard and a ticket.

What Is Missing? (page 59)

A. 6
B. 12
C. 17
D. 144; 9
E. 29
F. 81

Missing Numbers (page 60)

A. 5
B. 48
C. 6
D. 7; 16
3; 22
E. 7
F. 33

Something Is Missing (page 61)

A. 9
B. 33
C. 48
D. 68, 6
2, 27
E. 6
F. 128

Function Junction (page 62)

Function is F = 2n – 1

What Happened? (page 63)

Function is F = 2n – 3

Phone Numbers (page 64)

Function is F = 3n – 2

Magician's Shapes (page 65)

Rhombus

Marvyn's Shapes (page 66)

A. Prism
B. Right triangle
C. Oval

Shape Magic (page 67)

A. Octagon
B. Cylinder
C. Trapezoid

Circumference (page 68)

A. 20 inches
B. 226 inches

Tree Farm (page 69)

A. 44 inches
B. 132 inches
C. 3 inches
D. 18 inches

Wagon Wheels (page 70)

A. Diameter—58 inches
circumference—182 inches
B. Diameter—38 inches
circumference—119 inches
C. Diameter—28 inches
circumference—88 inches
D. Diameter—36 inches
circumference—113 inches

Triangles (page 71)

A. Right triangle; 30°

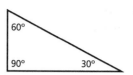

B. Equilateral triangle; 60°, 60°, 60°

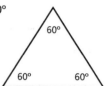

Triangles' Angles (page 72)

A. Obtuse triangle; 120°, 30°, 30°

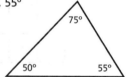

B. Acute triangle; 75°, 50°, 55°

C. Right triangle; 90°, 30°, 60°

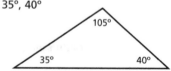

D. Obtuse triangle; 105°, 35°, 40°

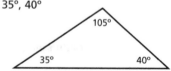

Assignment Triangles (page 73)

A. Right triangle; 90°, 55°, 35°

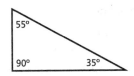

B. Acute triangle; 35°, 72.5°, 72.5°

C. Obtuse triangle; 95°, 40°, 45°

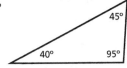

D. Equilateral triangle; 60°, 60°, 60°

Area (page 74)

A. 13 feet
B. 15 square feet

The Toy Store (page 75)

A. 1,473 square feet
B. 192 square feet
C. 7 feet
D. 4 feet

Playground (page 76)

A. 18 feet
B. 14 feet
C. 16 feet
D. 16 feet

Volume (page 77)

A. 8 inches
B. No, the planter needs 24,000 cm³ of potting soil.
   They will need a second bag.

The Terrarium (page 78)

A. 672 cubic inches
B. Yes, she needs 336 cubic inches.
C. 1,680 cubic inches; she will need 2 bags.

Playtime (page 79)

A. 54 cubic inches; 162 cubic inches
B. 64 cubic feet; 4 bags
C. 4 feet

Time (page 80)

A. 5 hours, 25 minutes
B. $37.50

Working (page 81)

A. 108 hours
B. $4.00
C. 48 days
D. leave home at 1:35 p.m. and arrive home at 3:40 p.m.

Travel Time (page 82)

A. 6 hours
B. 10 hours, 46 minutes
C. 14 hours, 33 minutes
D. 7 hours, 11 minutes

Are We There Yet? (page 83)

A. 780 miles
B. 1,199.25 yards

Traveling (page 84)

A. 50 mph
B. 414 miles
C. 20 miles
D. 6 hours, 40 minutes

Distance (page 85)

A. 240 miles
B. 167 days
C. 3.5 miles
D. 550 miles

Baking Cookies (page 86)

Cookie Recipe

A. <u>Two Dozen</u>
  ½ cup butter
  ¾ cup sugar
  1 egg
  1½ cups flour
  ½ cup walnuts
  ½ cup chocolate chips

B. <u>Twelve Dozen</u>
  3 cups butter
  4½ cups sugar
  6 eggs
  9 cups flour
  3 cups walnuts
  3 cups chocolate chips

Birthday Party (page 87)

A. **Lemonade** (50 Cups)
  25 lemons
  50 cups water
  5½ cups sugar

B. **Brownies** (Five Dozen)
  1⅔ cups unsweetened cocoa powder
  5 cups flour
  5 teaspoons baking powder
  2½ teaspoons salt
  2½ cups butter
  10 eggs
  8⅓ cups sugar

Pizza Fun (page 88)

Pizza Dough

<u>75 Pizzas</u>
67.5 cups warm water
75 tablespoons active yeast
75 teaspoons sugar
37.5 teaspoons salt
150 tablespoons oil
45 cups flour

Pizza Sauce

<u>75 Pizzas</u>
36 medium-sized tomatoes
9 onions
12 teaspoons sugar
30 teaspoons fresh basil
15 cloves garlic

How Much Do I Need? (page 89)

A. 12-ounce bag of egg noodles
B. six 6-ounce bags

Now You Are Cooking (page 90)

A. two 8-ounce bags plus eleven 4-ounce bags for a total of 60 ounces
B. one 800-gram can and one 400-gram can of tomato juice
C. five 2-liter bottles

In the Kitchen (page 91)

A. 20 ounces
B. 6.6 liters

The Sleepover (page 92)

A. $1.20
B. whole mushrooms—$0.31 per ounce
  sliced mushrooms—$0.69 per ounce
  Whole mushrooms are less expensive.

The Fruit Stand (page 93)

A. 12 pears; $0.42
B. 8 ounces
C. 2 packages
D. $10.20

Dinner Plans (page 94)

A. approximately 22 cents per ounce, needs 27 ounces, $5.94
B. 3 bunches and she will have some left over
C. 2¼ cups rice
D. three 1-pound containers plus one ½ pound container

Candy Store (page 95)

Name	Amount	Caramels	Balls	Drops	Squares	Rolls
Kira	$3.35	3	0	6	4	0
Ian	$3.00	4	2	0	2	2
Gwyn	$1.50	1	5	0	0	1

Park Lunch (page 96)

Order 1—Ryan
Order 2—Decker
Order 3—Coley
Order 4—Kali
Order 5—Anika
Order 6—Julie

School Supplies (page 97)

List 1—Maria
List 2—Jared
List 3—Betsy
List 4—Kris
List 5—Alyssa
List 6—Brodie

Ratio and Probability (page 98)

A. ⅔
   2:3
   2 to 3
B. $\frac{1}{23}$

Ratios (page 99)

A. 5/7   5:7   5 to 7
B. $^{12}/_{15}$ 12:15   12 to 15
C. $^{8}/_{27}$
D. $^{24}/_{72}$ (reduced to ⅓)

Comparing (page 100)

A. $^{28}/_{35}$ 28:35   28 to 35
B. $^{12}/_{14}$ (6/7)   12:14 (6:7)   12 to 14 (6 to 7)
C. $^{4}/_{52}$ (reduced to $\frac{1}{13}$) $^{13}/_{52}$ (reduced to ¼)
D. $\frac{1}{15}$ $^{3}/_{15}$ (reduced to ⅕)

Percentages (page 101)

A. $20
B. 875 students

Percents Are Fun (page 102)

A. 123 cards
B. $600
C. 359 stamps
D. 61 students

What Percent Is Left? (page 103)

A. $22.50
B. 1,880 pounds
C. 330 students
D. 540 tulips

Baseball Tournament (page 104)

9 games

Tennis Match (page 105)

11 games

All City Chess (page 106)

18 games

Ice-Cream Sundae (page 107)

15 flavor combinations

Your Order, Please (page 108)

28 combinations

School Colors (page 109)

45 color combinations

Camp Activities (page 110)

Swimming—70
Fishing—40
Canoeing—30
Archery—10
Hiking—50

Zoo Animals (page 111)

Mammals—157.5
Birds—54
Reptiles—45
Amphibians—22.5
Insects—112.5
Fish—36
Other—22.5

Favorite Subject (page 112)

Spelling—1.5
Reading—12
Math—3
Science—7.5
History—6

Favorite Colors (page 113)

Ashley—red
Olivia—pink
Ngan—blue
Latasha—green

Ice Cream (page 114)

Soren—chocolate
Silas—mint chocolate chip
Ruthann—peppermint
Victoria—vanilla
Julia—strawberry

Birthdays (page 115)

Mitchell—January
Kendall—October
Olivia—March
Madeline—April
Cody—May

Nicknames (page 116)

Julie—Bubbles
Pat—Slugger
Ty—Twinkle Toes
Peter—Sunshine
Debbie—Rocky

Bird Watching (page 117)

Dena—cardinal
Wendy—golden eagle
Steven—Canada goose
Carl—blue jay
Cindy—American robin

Toy Time (page 118)

Jayson—cars
Emily—action figure
Tom—baby doll
Marta—plush bear
Logan—blocks

Lunchtime (page 119)

Alice—chicken nuggets
Scott—cheeseburger
Linda—pepperoni pizza
Curtis—chef's salad
Joyce—Chinese steamed vegetables